THE OFFICIAL CARRY ON QUIZ BOOK

COMPILED BY CHRIS COWLIN AND PAUL BURTON

FOREWORDS BY NORMAN HUDIS AND JACKI PIPER

APEX PUBLISHING LTD

First published in 2007, updated and reprinted in 2008 and 2010 by
Apex Publishing Ltd
PO Box 7086, Clacton on Sea, Essex, CO15 5WN, England

www.apexpublishing.co.uk

British Library Cataloguing-in-Publication Data
A catalogue record for this book
is available from the British Library

ISBN 1-904444-97-0   978-1-904444-97-8

Typeset in 10.5pt Chianti BdIt Win95BT

Cover Design: Siobhan Smith
Photograph © FremantleMedia

Printed and bound in Great Britain

Authors' Note:
Please can you contact ChrisCowlin@btconnect.com if you find any
mistakes/errors in this book as Paul and I would like to put them right on any
future reprints. We would also like to hear from any *Carry On* fans who have
enjoyed the test! Visit my website: **www.ChrisCowlin.com**

FOREWORD

It's been said that of the making of books there is no end.

This needs to be amended to of the making of books about the Carry Ons there seems to be no end.

This one is different in that it invites the apparently fanatic admirer of the series to demonstrate how much he/she knows about the details of personalities, titles, dates etc.,

Frankly, I was stumped by most of the posers - but I figure I may be excused: perhaps it's enough to be a part of the whole story, by writing the first six, without being expected to be Mr Memory as well.

I hope this industriously accumulated volume sells as mightily as did the films themselves.

Norman Hudis
(Scriptwriter for the First Six Carry On Films)

FOREWORD

Forget Mastermind. Forget Brain of Britain. This is the quiz book to challenge all those Carry on fans out there! Lets face it They are a superior bunch!

This is the perfect quiz book for bringing a smile to your face as you remember all those ridiculous, outrageous and funny Carry On moments.

They say laughter is the best medicine so I prescribe this book to be read at least once a day!

Carry on smiling all of you and long live all the happy memories.

I think the book is fantastic. Chris and Paul have put a lot of work into this.

Love from
Jacki Piper xx

Jacki Piper
(Actress in *Carry On Loving*, *Carry On Up the Jungle*,
Carry On At Your Convenience and *Carry On Matron*)

INTRODUCTION
By Chris Cowlin

I would first of all like to thank Norman Hudis and Jacki Piper for writing the Forewords to this book. I am very grateful for their help on this project. I would also like to thank the following people for their comments and support: Nicholas Parsons, Dora Bryan OBE, Linda Regan, George Layton, Peter Byrne, Jack Douglas, Alan Hume, Don McCorkindale, Nosher Powell, Bill Pertwee MBE and Harry Fielder.

I would personally like to thank Peter Rogers (Pinewood Studios) and Naheed Arshad (Granada Ventures) who gave me the go-ahead to write the book. I actually started this project at the end of 2005 and eventually wrote to Mr Rogers at the start of 2007. I am glad also to have met Paul Burton, who has fantastic knowledge of TV and many programmes past and present. Every time I talk to him I learn so much - remembering it all is a problem!

I would also like to thank the following people and websites for their comments and help during the book's compilation: Kevin Snelgrove, Robert Ross, Morris Bright, www.bscw.co.uk, www.carryon.me.uk, www.thewhippitinn.com and www.carryonline. com.

I hope you enjoy this book. It was a TRUE pleasure compiling it, as the *Carry On* films are loved by every household. I am sure whatever section you choose to read first will make you smile and the memories will come flooding back. I have no doubt that after picking up this book you will want to watch each of the films all over again - as I did!

In closing, I would like to thank all my friends and family for encouraging me to complete this project.

Chris Cowlin.

Best wishes
Chris Cowlin

INTRODUCTION

By Paul Burton

My love of the Carry On films began way back in the early 1980s, when as a boy I discovered a compilation TV series entitled Carry On Laughing, created by the makers of the Carry On films, Peter Rogers and Gerald Thomas, for broadcast on the ITV network by Thames Television. These compilations were my gateway to a lifelong adoration of the comic exploits of the Carry On team.

As the '80s rolled on, my interest - indeed passion - for the Carry On films grew and grew. By now I had also discovered the various other theatre, film, television and radio work with which the Carry On team members were involved - especially Kenneth Williams, whose regular appearances on the TV chat show and game show circuit were a must-see for me.

By the time the Rank-funded Carry On films had been released on video in 1987, I was a total devotee of the films and of the Carry On gang. Every spare pound I had was put aside in order to save up to buy another film from the Carry On series on video.

In the late '80s I started to write to the offices of Peter Rogers (producer) and Gerald Thomas (director), and I was lucky enough to receive replies. This, of course, was during a period when regular press releases from their Pinewood bases declared that new Carry On films were to be made. However, for various reasons it would not be until 1992 that a new film was indeed made.

On waking up one morning during an Easter school holiday in the late '80s, I discovered to my delight that I had received a reply from one of my favourite *Carry On* film actors, Kenneth Williams. He had sent me a signed photo, a piece of notepaper and a copy of his book, *Back Drops*. I instantly wrote back to thank him, even adding a few questions, for instance: would he be in the planned new *Carry On* films as rumoured? Sadly, I did not receive a reply to this letter, and only a matter of days later it was announced that Kenneth Williams, aged 62, had been found dead in his London flat.

As the years have rolled on I've founded my own various arts projects, and it may or may not surprise you to know that my main inspiration for becoming involved in the arts came from the work of Rogers and Thomas.

Many of the *Carry On* team have sadly left us, as has the director of the films, Gerald Thomas. But, thank goodness, there are still members of the team left who continue to delight us with their various appearances.

Co-compiling this book has been an absolute joy. I feel both proud and lucky to have had the opportunity to work on this project. My almost lifelong obsession with the all of the various *Carry On* related productions, and the actors that have worked on them, has resulted in this: *The Official Carry On Quiz Book*. I am sure that co-author Chris Cowlin would agree with me that this book is fondly dedicated to those who have worked on all the different *Carry On* projects - both in the public eye and behind the scenes.

I hope you enjoy this book, and now it's time for me to "Stop messin' about" and for you to 'Carry On Guessing' and 'Carry On Laughing'!

Best wishes
Paul Burton

SID JAMES

1. In which country was Sid born?

2. What was the name of Sid's character in *Bless This House*?

3. True or false: Sid appeared in the film *What a Carve Up!* with fellow *Carry On* stars Kenneth Connor, Shirley Eaton and Esma Cannon?

4. In the early 1950s, in which radio show did Sid become a member of the cast?

5. What was the name of Sid's character in *Carry On Loving*?

6. True or false: Sid's parents were music-hall performers?

7. How much was Sid paid to play his part in *Carry On Regardless* - £2,000, £4,000 or £6,000?

8. In how many *Carry On* films did Sid star - 15, 17 or 19?

9. What was Sid's last *Carry On* film?

10. What was the name of Sid's character in *Carry On At Your Convenience*?

CARRY ON AGAIN DOCTOR

11. In what year was the film released - 1965, 1967 or 1969?

12. Which character was played by Barbara Windsor?

13. True or false: actress Valerie Van Ost played an out-patient's sister?

14. Who directed this film?

15. What was the name of the hospital in the film?

16. Which actor played character Dr James Nookey?

17. Which actress played Matron?

18. What was the name of the character played by Sid James?

19. Which actress played Miss Fosdick?

20. True or false: Pat Coombs played the character Nurse Willing?

BARBARA WINDSOR

21. In how many *Carry On* films did Barbara star - 5, 7 or 9?

22. Which was Barbara's first *Carry On* film?

23. Following on from the previous question, what was her character's name?

24. Where was Barbara born - London, Nottingham or Leeds?

25. Which soap did Barbara join in 1995?

26. Following on from the previous question, what is her character's name?

27. In 1954, in which film did Barbara make her debut?

28. Name Barbara's last *Carry On* film to date.

29. What was the name of Barbara's character in *Carry On Henry*?

30. In which *Carry On* film did Barbara star in 1967?

MATCH THE DATE - 1

Match up the event with the date it happened

31.	Sally Douglas was born	1992
32.	Carry On Nurse was released	1943
33.	Carry On Behind was released	1995
34.	Dany Robin sadly passed away	1976
35.	Margaret Nolan was born	1975
36.	Carry On Henry was released	1991
37.	Sid James sadly passed away	1959
38.	Anna Karen was born	1971
39.	Bob Todd sadly passed away	1942
40.	Carry On Columbus was released	1936

CARRY ON ABROAD

41.   In what year was this film released - 1970, 1971 or 1972?

42.   True or false: actress Carol Hawkins played Marge in this film?

43.   Which character was played by Barbara Windsor?

44.   What was the profession of Vic Flange, played by Sid James?

45.   Which actor played the character Stuart Farquhar?

46.   What was the name of the hotel that was featured in the film?

47.   What was the name of the hotel cook?

48.   Which well-known actress played Evelyn Blunt?

49.   Following on from the previous question, what was the name of Evelyn Blunt's husband?

50.   True or false: Jack Douglas starred in the film and played a character called Harry?

KENNETH CONNOR

51. In how many *Carry On* films did Kenneth appear - 16, 17 or 18?

52. What was the profession of Kenneth's character, Bernie Bishop, in the film *Carry On Nurse*?

53. What was the name of Kenneth's character, who suffered badly from hypochondria, in the film *Carry On Sergeant*?

54. Which hugely talented actress played Kenneth's wife, Senna, in the film *Carry On Cleo* - Sheila Hancock, Patsy Rowlands or June Whitfield?

55. Kenneth's real-life son, Jeremy, took a small cameo role as his son in the film *Carry On Nurse*, but in which three other *Carry On* films did Jeremy later appear with his father?

56. Kenneth made a particularly early stage debut, but exactly how old was he - 1, 2 or 3?

57. In which highly successful West End musical did Kenneth star opposite fellow *Carry On* actor Frankie Howerd?

58. True or false: Kenneth once appeared in the sitcom *Dad's Army*?

59. What does Kenneth's character in *Carry On Matron* suggest that the doctors at Finisham Maternity Hospital use to induce labour in his wife?

60. What was the name of the character played by Rosalind Knight in *Carry On Teacher* for whom Kenneth's character, Mr Adams, eventually declares his love?

THAT'S CARRY ON

61.   Where was all the linking material shot for this film compilation?

62.   What is Kenneth dying to do all the way through the film?

63.   Which of the *Carry On* films, already made by the time this film was made, did not have any clips featured in this hugely entertaining compilation film?

64.   When was the shooting for this film completed - February 1977, March 1977 or April 1977?

65.   True or false: Talbot Rothwell wrote the linking material for this film?

66.   What was the tag line for this film?

67.   Who arranged the music for this compilation film - Bruce Montgomery, Eric Rogers or Max Harris?

68.   What film certificate did this film have?

69.   In what month and year was this compilation film released - January 1978, February 1978 or March 1978?

70.   What does Barbara Windsor do to Kenneth Williams at the very end of the film?

CARRY ON DICK

71. This film was sadly to be the last to have its screenplay written by Talbot Rothwell, but on whose treatment is this film based?

72. What was the name of the public house in the film?

73. What is the name of the former Miss World who played one of the Birds of Paradise in this film - Laraine Humphreys, Linda Hooks or Eva Reuber-Staier?

74. Which future star of the BBC sitcom *'Allo 'Allo!* played Sir Roger Daley's coachman in this film?

75. What was the name of the inept sergeant played by Jack Douglas in this film?

76. Which long-time *Carry On* team actress played the role of Martha Hoggett in this film?

77. What was the Reverend Flasher (played by Sid James in his last *Carry On* film) so keen to get into use once more - the church font, the church bells or the church organ?

78. Which actress played Bernard Bresslaw's wife, Lady Daley, in this film?

79. What was the profession of Kenneth Williams' character in this film?

80. True or false: *Are You Being Served?* actress, Wendy Richard, appeared in this film?

JIM DALE

81. What small role did Jim play in his first *Carry On* film, *Carry On Cabby* - a taxi driver, an expectant father or a car mechanic?

82. What was originally the profession of Jim's character in the film *Carry On Cowboy* before he became Marshall P. Knutt?

83. What leisurely past-time did Jim's character, Dr Nookie, have in *Carry On Again Doctor* whilst coping with life in the Beatific Isles?

84. Which actress played Jim's girlfriend in the films *Carry On Cowboy*, *Carry On Screaming* and *Carry On Follow That Camel* - Anita Harris, Angela Douglas or Jacki Piper?

85. How many years were there between Jim's last two *Carry On* films, *Carry On Again Doctor* and *Carry On Columbus*?

86. In how many *Carry On* films did Jim actually appear?

87. True or false: Jim appeared in the 1969 Thames Television *Carry On* TV spin-off, *Carry On Christmas*?

88. In which *Carry On* film did Jim appear during 1966 which originally did not have the *Carry On* prefix in its title?

89. True or false: Jim appeared in the Rogers and Thomas *Carry On* film, *Nurse On Wheels*, which starred John Mills' daughter, Juliet?

90. Name the West End musical that Jim starred in alongside fellow *Carry On* star, Patsy Rowlands, at the London Palladium.

PETER GILMORE

91. What role did Peter play in his first *Carry On* film?

92. True or false: Peter appeared in the film *Carry On Camping*?

93. In how many *Carry On* films did Peter star - 9, 10 or 11?

94. What fruit is Peter's character, Henry, consuming when he first meets Barbara Windsor's character, Nurse Sandra May, in *Carry On Doctor*?

95. What rank did Peter's character have in the film *Carry On Cleo*?

96. True or false: Peter once appeared in the TV series, *A Man Called Intrepid*?

97. Which popular *Carry On* actress played Peter's garlic-obsessed cousin in the film *Carry On Henry*?

98. Peter starred briefly as a Private in *Carry On Up The Khyber*, but what was the name of his character?

99. What was the name of Peter's last *Carry On* film?

100. In which *Carry On* film did Peter play the character Citizen Rosepierre?

BILL MAYNARD

101. Which character did Bill play in *Carry On At Your Convenience?*

102. In how many *Carry On* films did Bill appear - 4, 5 or 6?

103. Following on from the previous question, can you name three of them?

104. In which *Carry On* film did Bill play a character called Guy Fawkes?

105. What was the name of Bill's character in the police drama *Heartbeat?*

106. In which '*Confessions of ...*' film, made in 1977, did Bill appear?

107. What is the name of Bill's autobiography?

108. At which holiday camp was Bill a singer at the start of his career?

109. In what year was Bill born - 1920, 1924 or 1928?

110. In which *Carry On* film was Bill cast as Mr Fiddler, although the scene was later cut?

CARRY ON BEHIND

111. Which actor played the Doctor in the film?

112. Where did Fred Ramsden and Ernie Bragg tell their wives they were going?

113. In which year was this film released in colour?

114. What was the name of the caravan site featured in the film?

115. Which ex-*Dad's Army* and *EastEnders* actor played Joe Baxter?

116. Which university were Professor Roland Crump and his students from?

117. Following on from the previous question, what was the name of the female professor who joined them, played by actress Elke Sommer?

118. True or false: Barbara Windsor starred in the film and played character Carol?

119. Which character was played by Bernard Bresslaw?

120. Which actress played the mother-in-law of the character Arthur Upmore?

JACK DOUGLAS

121. In how many *Carry On* films did Jack appear - 5, 8 or 13?

122. True or false: Jack appeared in the TV sitcom, *The Shillingbury Tales*?

123. What is Jack most famous for in the *Carry On* films?

124. What was Jack's first *Carry On* film in 1972?

125. True or false: Jack appeared in *Carry On Columbus*?

126. What was Jack's father's profession?

127. Where in the country was Jack born in 1927 - Nottingham, Newcastle or Northampton?

128. True or false: Jack played Bombardier Ready in *Carry On England*?

129. In which *Carry On* film did Jack play a character called William?

130. True or false: One of Jack's most favourite hobbies is cooking?

HATTIE JACQUES

131. What was Hattie's first *Carry On* film, in which she played Captain Clark?

132. In which long-running BBC TV sitcom did Hattie regularly appear - *The Rag Trade*, *Sykes* or *Dad's Army*.

133. Which actor played the husband of Hattie's character in *Carry On Loving*?

134. Following on from the previous question, what was the name of Hattie's character in the film?

135. In how many *Carry On* films did Hattie appear - 10, 14 or 18?

136. In what year was Hattie born in Kent - 1904, 1914 or 1924?

137. In which 1963 *Carry On* film did Hattie play the character Peggy?

138. What was the name of Hattie's character in *Carry On At Your Convenience*?

139. What is the name of the actor to whom Hattie was once married?

140. Which *Carry On* film was Hattie's last?

CARRY ON COLUMBUS

141.   In which year was this film released?

142.   Which well-known actress played Countess Esmeralda?

143.   True or false: Barbara Windsor played a character called Fatima?

144.   Which character was played by Leslie Phillips?

145   Who was the producer of the film?

146.   Which well-known actor and comedian played the Sultan?

147.   Which actor 'Martin' played character Martin?

148.   True or false: June Whitfield played Queen Isabella in the film?

149.   Which actor played Christopher Columbus?

150.   Which character was played by Burt Kwouk?

NORMAN HUDIS

151. How many *Carry On* films did Norman Hudis write?

152. Which of the *Carry On* screenplays that Norman wrote did he consider to be his least favourite?

153. True or false: Norman wrote a film script called *Carry On Again Nurse*?

154. Name the last *Carry On* screenplay that Norman wrote that was filmed.

155. Which of the *Carry On* films that Norman wrote did he consider his best screenplay?

156. Which of the following *Carry On* films did Norman not write - *Carry On Nurse, Carry On Teacher* or *Carry On Jack*?

157. Name the other Rogers and Thomas film that Norman wrote and which featured a reference to daffodils.

158. True or false: Norman later wrote material for the stage show, *Carry On London*?

159. In which year was Norman born?

160. Which real-life police station was Norman sent to in order to study police procedure before writing *Carry On Constable*?

PETER ROGERS

161. True or false: Peter wrote a play called *Human Straw*, which was staged for a short run at the Players' Theatre in London?

162. Name the rock and roll singer on whose biopic Peter acted as executive producer in 1957.

163. Which of the following films was Peter not involved in - *Please Turn Over, Cat Girl* or *Trouble in Store*?

164. In which year did Peter make the film *Watch Your Stern*?

165. True of false: Peter once worked as a scriptwriter at Gainsborough Studios?

166. Peter married which film producer on 24 December 1948?

167. What was the nickname that Peter gave to the director of the *Carry On* films, Gerald Thomas?

168. True or false: Peter was an associate producer on the film *Appointment With Venus*, which starred David Niven?

169. What was the name of the first Peter Rogers production directed by future *Carry On* film director, Gerald Thomas?

170. On which of the following dates was Peter born - 20 January 1914, 20 February 1914 or 20 March 1914?

POT LUCK - 1

171. What was the name of Renée Houston's first *Carry On* film - *Carry On Nurse, Carry On Regardless* or *Carry On Cabby*?

172. True or false: Julian Holloway played one of Lady Ponsonby's many lovers in the film *Carry On Follow That Camel*?

173. On which TV quiz show did *Carry On* supporting actress Linda Hooks once appear as a hostess?

174. What was the name of Frankie Howerd's Oozalum bird obsessed character in the film *Carry On Up the Jungle*?

175. True or false: Patricia Hayes played Jenny Grubb's strict mother in *Carry On Loving*?

176. For which of the following *Carry On* films did actor and pop singer David Essex film a scene that sadly ended up on the cutting room floor - *Carry On Loving, Carry On Henry,* or *Carry On Abroad*?

177. Who delivered the commentary for the film *Carry On Cleo*?

178. What was the name of Bernard Bresslaw's jealous wrestler character in the film *Carry On Loving*?

179. In how many *Carry On* films did Terry Scott appear?

180. Which *Dad's Army* actor filmed a scene for the film *Carry On Loving*, which sadly did not make the final cut?

CARRY ON EMMANNUELLE

181. What was the name of Joan Sims' character in this film?

182. Who wrote the screenplay for this film?

183. True or false: *Carry On* actor Norman Mitchell played a drunken sailor in this film?

184. Which of the following actors, best known for appearing in *The Benny Hill Show*, also appeared in this film - Bob Todd, Henry McGee or Jon Jon Keefe?

185. What fee was Kenneth Williams reportedly paid for appearing in this film?

186. Which actress, who later went on to appear in the Cannon and Ball film *The Boys in Blue*, played Emmannuelle Prevert in this film?

187. Who wrote the song that can be heard at the beginning and end of this film?

188. What is the running length of this film - 86 minutes, 87 minutes or 88 minutes?

189. Which actress played Theodore Valentine's mother in this film?

190. What certificate was the film originally given when released in 1978?

GERALD THOMAS

191. At which film studio did Gerald start his career in the film industry?

192. True or false: Gerald's brother, Ralph Thomas, established the *Doctor* film series with Peter Rogers' wife, Betty E. Box?

193. In which year was Gerald born - 1920, 1921 or 1922?

194. What was the name of the TV compilation series that Gerald completed shortly before he died?

195. True or false: Gerald was born in Hull, Yorkshire?

196. Gerald directed a film version of a Thames TV sitcom in 1972. Name it.

197. What did Gerald donate to the British Film Institute in 1993?

198. What was the name of the BBC Radio 2 series, which featured Kenneth Connor as its subject, that Gerald took part in as a guest in the late '80s?

199. Which of the following films did Gerald not direct during his long career in the industry - *Nurse On Wheels*, *Dentist in the Chair* or *Time Lock*?

200. In which year did Gerald sadly pass away?

MATCH THE DATE - 2

Match up the event with the date it happened

201.	*Carry On Cowboy* was released	1980
202.	Angela Douglas was born	1970
203.	*Carry On Cleo* was released	1987
204.	George Layton appeared in his only *Carry On* film	1985
205.	*Carry On Loving* was released	1965
206.	Imogen Hassall sadly passed away	2003
207.	Arthur Lovegrove sadly passed away	1940
208.	Thirteen Rank-financed *Carry On* films were released onto video	1975
209.	Bob Monkhouse sadly passed away	1964
210.	Barbara Windsor appeared in the stage show *What a Carry On!*	1981

PETER BUTTERWORTH

211.   What was Peter's first *Carry On* film?

212.   Following on from the previous question, what was his character's name in the film?

213.   In how many *Carry On* films did Peter appear - 6, 16 or 26?

214.   What was the name of Peter's character in *Carry On Camping*?

215.   True or false: Peter appeared in *Carry On Emmannuelle* and played the character Richmond?

216.   In what year was Peter born in Manchester - 1909, 1919 or 1929?

217.   Can you name Peter's wife, who is an actress, comedienne and impressionist?

218.   In which film did Peter appear in 1972, playing Trevor Lewis, alongside Sid James?

219.   Which character did Peter play in *Carry On Henry*?

220.   In which *Carry On* film did Peter play Brother Belcher?

CARRY ON CONSTABLE

221. In which year was this film released in black and white?

222. Which actress played character Sally Barry?

223. Which actor played PC Stanley Benson?

224. Was *Carry On Constable* the 4th, 5th or 6th *Carry On* film?

225. Which character did Sid James play?

226. Which actor played PC Tom Potter?

227. In how many *Carry On* films had Charles Hawtrey appeared before this one?

228. True or false: Joan Hickson played a character called Mrs May?

229. True or false: Scottish comedian Chic Murray was originally considered for the role of Sergeant Frank Wilkins?

230. Which character was played by actress Jill Adams?

MATCH THE DATE - 3

Match up the event with the date it happened

231. Barbara Windsor took her one-women
     show, *Carry On Barbara*, to Australia
     and New Zealand   1978

232. Bill Cunnings appeared in his
     only *Carry On* film   1987

233. Harry Locke sadly passed away   1912

234. *Carry on Abroad* was premiered   1958

235. Jerry Desmonde sadly passed away   1964

236. Patricia Hayes appeared in her
     only *Carry On* film   1992

237. Bill Pertwee appeared in his last
     Carry On film   1967

238. Leigh Madison appeared in her
     first *Carry On* film   1973

239. Wilfred Brambell was born   1969

240. Toby Dale appeared in his only
     Carry On film to date   1975

TERRY SCOTT

241. Which *Carry On* film was Terry's first?

242. Following on from the previous question, what was the name of Terry's character?

243. In what year was Terry born - 1923, 1925 or 1927?

244. In how many *Carry On* films did Terry appear?

245. In which *Carry On* film did Terry play Cardinal Wolsey?

246. What was name of Terry's character in *Carry On Loving*?

247. Which well-known actress did Terry work with in the TV series *Terry & June*?

248. Terry played a doctor in *Carry On Matron*, but what was his name?

249. True or false: Terry appeared in the *Bless this House* film with Sid James?

250. In what year did Terry sadly pass away?

JULIAN HOLLOWAY

251. Which item of Barbara Windsor's clothing did Julian accidentally pull off in the film *Carry On Camping*?

252. What was the name of Julian's character in the film *Carry On England*?

253. In which of the following *Carry On* films did Julian not appear - *Carry On Screaming*, *Carry On Doctor* or *Carry On Loving*?

254. True of false: Julian appeared in the Big Screen version of the sitcom *Porridge*?

255. What is Julian's full name?

256. In which year was Julian born - 1942, 1943 or 1944?

257. In which year did Julian appear in a *Carry On Christmas* TV special - 1972, 1973 or 1974?

258. True or false: Julian played the role of Alfred P. Doolittle in the musical *My Fair Lady* on Broadway?

259. At which drama school did Julian train to become an actor?

260. True or false: Julian appeared in the film *Carry On Matron*?

CARRY ON SERGEANT

261. Terence Longdon played which character in this film?

262. True or false: Terry Scott played a small cameo role in this film?

263. This film was based on a script originally called *The Bull Boys*, but who wrote the aforementioned screen play?

264. Who wrote additional material for this film?

265. Which band played the music featured in this film?

266. True or false: the composer of the music featured in this film, Bruce Montgomery, was also a popular detective fiction writer?

267. Which of the follow actors did not appear in this film - Bill Owen, Bob Monkhouse or Leslie Phillips?

268. How much did this film cost to make?

269. How long did this film take to shoot?

270. How many pages did the first draft of the screenplay for this film have - 160, 170 or 180?

CARRY ON LONDON
- THE REVUE

271. Where did this revue originally premiere?

272. Which of the following *Carry On* team actors did not appear in this stage show - Kenneth Williams, Kenneth Connor or Bernard Bresslaw?

273. Who was the executive producer of this revue?

274. True or false: Talbot Rothwell wrote all of the material for this stage show?

275. At which London theatre was this show staged following its try-out run?

276. How long did this stage show run for in London?

277. True or false: the comedy director of this show, Bill Robertson, was the brother of *Carry On* team member, Jack Douglas?

278. How much was the costume budget on this show - £40,000, £50,000 or £60,000?

279. Which television company filmed this stage show and broadcast edited highlights on ITV?

280. Which host presented *Open House*, a BBC radio show in which the cast of *Carry On London* took part one morning in order to promote the London run of the revue?

CARRY ON LAUGHING
- TV SERIES

281. Which of the following ITV companies made the *Carry On* Laughing TV series in the mid-1970s - Thames TV, ATV or Yorkshire TV?

282. In how many editions of the series did Sid James appear?

283. Complete the title of the second edition of this series: *The Baron* _____.

284. True or false: Hattie Jacques appeared in an edition of the series entitled *Orgy and Bess*?

285. Which of the following British actors had his role cut out of the edition of the series entitled *Orgy and Bess* - Victor Maddern, Brian Osborne or Simon Callow?

286. Which regular *Carry On* film actor played the role of Sir Pureheart in an edition of this TV series called *Under the Round Table*?

287. True or false: future *Emmerdale* actress Sherrie Hewson played a character called Virginia in an edition of this *Carry On* TV series called *Lamp-Posts of the Empire*?

288. How many editions of this series were made in the mid-1970s - 13, 14 or 15?

289. Which of the following *Carry On* teams members did not appear in this TV series - Peter Butterworth, Kenneth Williams or Barbara Windsor?

290. True or false: actor Oscar James appeared in the edition of this series entitled *Under the Round Table*?

CARRY ON NURSE

291. On what stage play was this film loosely based?

292. What type of student did Kenneth Williams play in this film?

293. What was the name of the men's ward in this film?

294. Which of the following actresses played Jack Bell's girlfriend in this film - June Whitfield, Jill Ireland or Rosalind Knight?

295. What is the running time of this film?

296. What certificate was this film originally released with?

297. What is the profession of the character Ted York in this film?

298. True or false: the uniforms for this film were provided by a company called Courtaulds?

299. Which *Carry On* actress played Nurse Stella Dawson in this film?

300. What type of flower did two of the nurses decide to use to take the Colonel's temperature at the end of the film?

APPEARANCES

*Match up the actors/actresses with the number of
Carry On films they have appeared in*

301.	Liz Fraser	1
302.	Donald Hewlett	2
303.	Larry Dann	2
304.	Windsor Davies	4
305.	Derek Francis	2
306.	Ian Curry	8
307.	Julian Holloway	2
308.	Anne Scott	4
309.	Wanda Ventham	2
310.	Richard O'Callaghan	6

CARRY ON CRUISING

311. Which actor played Captain Wellington Crowther?

312. This film was released in 1962, but was it the fifth, sixth or seventh *Carry On* film?

313. Which actress played character Flo Castle?

314. Which character was attracted to passenger Flo Castle?

315. What was the name of the ship in the film?

316. Which character was played by Kenneth Williams?

317. What role did Jill Mai Meredith play in the film?

318. True or false: Glad Trimble was played by actress Marian Collins?

319. At the end of the film a party is thrown to celebrate how many years since the captain took charge of the ship - 5, 10 or 15?

320. True or false: Barbara Windsor appeared in the film and played character Bridget Madderley?

LOCATIONS - 1

Match up the film with its filming location

321.	Maidenhead Town Hall	*Carry On Constable*
322.	Waddesdon Manor, Bucks	*Carry On Girls*
323.	Beaconsfield Church Bucks	*Carry On Teacher*
324.	Beddgelert, Snowdonia North Wales	*Carry On Follow That Camel*
325.	Hanwell Parish Church	*Carry On Don't Lose Your Head*
326.	Drayton Secondary School, Drayton Gardens, West Ealing	*Carry On Up the Kyber*
327.	Camber Sands, Rye, Sussex	*Carry On Again Doctor*
328.	Town Hall, Slough	*Carry On Sergeant*
329.	The Palace Hotel, Brighton	*Carry On Matron*
330.	Heatherwood Hospital, Ascot, Bucks	*Carry On At Your Convenience*

CARRY ON HENRY

331. In which year was this film released?

332. Which actor played King Henry VIII?

333. Can you name the actor who played a farmer in this film?

334. Which actor played Francis, King of France?

335. Was this film first released in black and white or colour?

336. True or false: The role of Bidet in this film was played by Gertan Klauber?

337. True or false: actor Douglas Ridley appeared in this film as Conte di Pisa?

338. True or false: one of the King Henry VIII's costume cloaks was originally worn by Richard Burton in a film?

339. Which actress played Henry's second wife in the film?

340. Which character was played by Kenneth Williams?

MATCH THE CHARACTER - 1

Match up the actor/actress with the character played

341.   Bob Monkhouse   Peter Golightly
                                                        (Carry On Sergeant)

342.   Patrick Cargill   Sergeant Ernie Nocker
      (Carry On Follow That Camel)

343.   Wendy Richard   Annie Oakley
      (Carry On Cowboy)

344.   Charles Hawtrey   Charlie Sage
      (Carry On Sergeant)

345.   Dianna MacNamara   Ida Downs
      (Carry On Girls)

346.   Angela Douglas   Felicity Wheeler
      (Carry On Teacher)

347.   Charles Hawtrey   Inspector Mills
      (Carry On Constable)

348.   Phil Silvers   Captain Le Pice
      (Carry On Follow That Camel)

349.   Eric Baker   Spanish Governor
      (Carry On Jack)

350.   Rosalind Knight   Princess Stephanie
      (Carry On Don't Lose Your Head)

CARRY ON TEACHER

351. Which future star of the classic sitcom, *Man About the House*, played the role of Robin Stevens in this film?

352. Actor Larry Dann, who appeared in this film, also played roles in which other three films in the series?

353. True or false: actor George Howell played the role of the school caretaker in this film?

354. Which *Carry On* actor played the role of Mr Bean in this film - Terence Longdon, Kenneth Williams or Charles Hawtrey?

355. Which of the following *Carry On* actresses did not appear in this film - Hattie Jacques, Liz Fraser or Rosalind Knight?

356. True or false: actress Carol White appeared in this film?

357. What was the name of Kenneth Williams' character in this film?

358. In which month and year was this film released?

359. How many days did it take to shoot this film - 40, 41 or 42?

360. What was the name of the fictitious school featured in this film?

CARRY ON CHRISTMAS
- TV SPECIALS

361. Which two roles did Frankie Howerd play in the 1969 *Carry On Christmas* TV special?

362. True or false: Peter Butterworth played the role of Dr Livershake in the 1970 Christmas TV special, *Carry On Again Christmas*?

363. Which of the following *Carry On* actors did not appear in *Carry On Stuffing*, first shown in 1972 - Peter Butterworth, Jack Douglas or Sid James?

364. What was the name of Sid James's character who played Santa Claus in the 1973 edition of *Carry On Christmas*?

365. True or false: actress Linda Regan briefly appeared in *Carry On Again Christmas* in 1970?

366. Which of the following roles did Joan Sims not play in *Carry On Christmas* in 1973 - Virginia, Adele or Maid Marian?

367. Which future *EastEnders'* actress appeared in *Carry On Again Christmas*?

368. What was the running time (without commercial breaks) of *Carry On Christmas* taped back in 1969?

369. True or false: Bernard Bresslaw played the role of Captain Ffying-Burgh in *Carry On Christmas* made by Thames Television in 1973?

370. What role did Norman Rossington play in the pantomime sketch in *Carry On Christmas* (also known as *Carry On Stuffing*) made in 1972?

WOT A CARRY ON IN BLACKPOOL!

371. True or false: this stage show was presented by Mike Hughes for Liver Promotions Ltd?

372. Which two *Carry On* team members starred in this show?

373. True or false: Barry Cryer was the co-writer of this show?

374. In which year was this show staged?

375. On which pier in Blackpool was the show staged?

376. True or false, performer Terry Gauntlett was billed in the programme as being the Light Comedy Relief?

377. Which of the following people devised and directed this show - Windsor Davies, Tudor Davies or Phil Davies?

378. True or false: the juvenile lead in the show was played by Andrew Grainger?

379. How many performances of this show were staged per night?

380. On what date was the final performance of this show staged?

CARRY ON REGARDLESS

381. What was the name of the agency run by Bert Handy in this film?

382. Which actress, who later appeared in *Carry On Screaming*, played the small role of Penny Panting in this film?

383. Which actor that appeared in *Carry On Regardless* later took a main role in the BBC detective series *Bergerac*?

384. True or false: actor Patrick Cargill, who later starred in the Thames TV sitcom *Father, Dear Father*, appeared in this film?

385. What did the poster tag line for this film declare?

386. Which of the following *Carry On* actresses did not appear in this film - Liz Fraser, Joan Sims or Hattie Jacques?

387. True or false: *Round the Horne* actress Betty Marsden appeared briefly in this film?

388. What was the name of the real-life boxer who appeared in this film?

389. What was the name of Terence Longdon's character in this film?

390. What was the name of the future *Last of the Summer Wine* actor who played Miles Weston in this film?

WHAT'S A CARRY ON?

391. True or false: *Carry On* actor Lance Percival was interviewed for this TV documentary?

392. Which of the following *Carry On* film stars was not interviewed for this TV documentary - Kenneth Connor, Jim Dale or Joan Sims?

393. Which British actor, who played the role of Jacko in the BBC sitcom *Brush Strokes*, appears in this TV documentary?

394. In what year was this TV documentary first shown?

395. On which TV channel was this documentary first broadcast?

396. Which of the following *Carry On* stars appeared in the final clip of this documentary - Charles Hawtrey, Kenneth Williams or Peter Butterworth?

397. Which veteran comedian, who has not appeared in a *Carry On* film, can be seen conducting an auction in this TV documentary?

398. Which two *Carry On* team members were interviewed for this TV documentary in the British seaside resort of Brighton?

399. Which of the following *Carry On* screenplay writers appeared in this TV documentary - Norman Hudis, Dave Freeman or Talbot Rothwell?

400. Name the *Carry On* actress who was interviewed for this TV documentary whilst on small boat.

CARRY ON CABBY

401. What was the name of Sid James's character?

402. Following on from the previous question, what was the name of his wife in the film, played by actress Hattie Jacques?

403. Can you name the actress who played Flo Sims?

404. What is the name of the taxi company owned by Sid James's character?

405. Hattie Jacques's character started a rival taxi company, but what did she call it?

406. Which actor played Terry 'Pintpot' Tankard?

407. When the film was released in 1963 was it in black and white or colour?

408. True or false: Amanda Barrie played a character called Sally?

409. Which actor played Allbright in this film - Norman Chappell, Jim Dale or Kenneth Connor?

410. What type of cars did the newly formed taxi company use?

CARRY ON GIRLS

411. What was the name of Barbara Windsor's character in the film?

412. Which actor, who played Peter Potter, dressed up as a woman?

413. What event did Sidney Fiddler organise?

414. What was the name of Kenneth Connor's character in this film?

415. Which actor played Cecil Gaybody?

416. In what year was this film released in colour?

417. Which actress played Mildred Bumble?

418. Margaret Nolan played a character called Dawn Brakes. What colour was the bikini she wore whilst sitting on a donkey?

419. What was the name of June Whitfield's character?

420. What was the name of the seaside resort where the story was based?

MATCH THE CHARACTER - 2

Match up the actor/actress with the character played

421. **Brian Oulton** **Harold Crump**
(Carry On Spying)

422. **Barbara Windsor** **Delia King**
(Carry On Regardless)

423. **Joan Sims** **Doris Mann**
(Carry On Screaming)

424. **Bernard Cribbins** **Sid Carter**
(Carry On Matron)

425. **Liz Fraser** **Daphne Honeybutt**
(Carry On Spying)

426. **Sid James** **Mordecai Mendoza**
(Carry On Columbus)

427. **Bernard Cribbins** **Henry Bray**
(Carry On Nurse)

428. **Angela Douglas** **Emily Bung**
(Carry On Screaming)

429. **Kenneth Williams** **Sergeant Len Able**
(Carry On England)

430. **Patrick Mower** **Oliver Reckitt**
(Carry On Nurse)

CARRY ON DOCTOR

431. Who was hired as a stunt double for Barbara Windsor?

432. Which actor played Francis Bigger?

433. What was the name of the hospital in the film?

434. Which actor played Dr Jim Kilmore?

435. What was the name of Sid James's character?

436. What pictures did Francis Bigger have on his underpants, which were removed by Matron?

437. Following on from the previous question, who played the Matron?

438. True or false: this film was released in 1965?

439. Which actress played Nurse Sandra May?

440. Which actor played Dr Kenneth Tinkle?

LOCATIONS - 2

Match up the film with its filming location

441.	Bourne End, Bucks		Carry On Regardless
442.	Park Street, Windsor, Bucks		Carry On Constable
443.	Southampton Docks		Carry On Behind
444.	Courts Shop, St. Ives High Street,		Carry On At Your Convenience
445.	Black Park Road Fulmer, Bucks		Carry On Abroad
446.	Lothair Road, Ealing		Carry On Camping
447.	Car Park at Pinewood		Carry On Emmannuelle
448.	11 Clarence Road, Windsor, Berks		Carry On Loving
449.	Farnham Common, Bucks		Carry On Cruising
450.	Odeon Cinema, Uxbridge		Carry On Cabby

POT LUCK - 2

451. How many *Carry On* films were made in colour between 1958 and 1992?

452. True or false: actress Liz Fraser appeared in the film *Carry On England*?

453. In how many *Carry On* films did actor Richard O'Callaghan appear - 1, 2 or 3?

454. What was the name of the health farm featured in the stage farce *Carry On Laughing in the Slimming Factory*?

455. The stage revue *Carry On London* featured a section in the show that paid tribute to which former Music Hall?

456. True or false: *Carry On Screaming* has the longest running time of all of the *Carry On* films to date?

457. How many scenes are there in the film *Carry On Camping* - 177, 180 or 184?

458. How did Jim Dale injure his arm during the making of *Carry On Again Doctor*?

459. In how many *Carry On* films did *Dad's Army* actor Bill Pertwee appear?

460. In what year did Noel Dyson, who appeared in two of the early *Carry On* films, sadly die?

CARRY ON JACK

461. Which actor played First Officer Jonathan Howett in this film?

462. True or false: this film was originally released with an 'A' certificate?

463. Which of the following *Carry On* team members did not appear in this film - Kenneth Williams, Bernard Bresslaw or Jim Dale?

464. What was the name of actor Ed Devereaux's character in this film?

465. Which actress, who had appeared in other *Carry On* films, was originally to have played the role of Sally in this film?

466. True or false: the title of this film was originally meant to be *Carry On Up the Armada*?

467. Which future *Fresh Fields'* actor played the small role of Hardy in this film?

468. Through which distribution company was this film originally released?

469. True or false: actress Marianne Stone played one of the girls at Dirty Dicks in this film?

470. Which actor played the role of Mr Angel the Bosun in this film?

CARRY ON FILMS
THAT WERE NEVER MADE

471. What was to have been the name of the film that was originally planned to have been made in Australia in 1988?

472. In what year did the makers of the film series originally plan to make a film called *Carry On Flying* - 1960, 1961 or 1962?

473. True or false: a film called *Carry On Spaceman* was considered in 1962?

474. What was to have been the budget of the projected *Carry On* film that was due to be made in Australia?

475. In 1979, the planned *Carry On Again Nurse* was set to become the 31st *Carry On* film in the series, but who were the chosen writers for this screenplay?

476. Name the title of the never made film for which actor Don Maclean (who later had a small cameo role in *Carry On Columbus*) wrote the screenplay.

477. Back in 1987, Russ Abbot, Victoria Wood and Lenny Henry were said to have been considered to take part in an ultimately unmade film, but what was it called?

478. True or false: Gerald Thomas travelled to Scotland to look at locations for a proposed *Carry On* film?

479. True or false: the makers of the film series, Peter Rogers and Gerald Thomas, were sent the idea for a film called *Carry On Stamp Collecting*?

480. The shelved film *Carry On Smoking* was to have been made in which year - 1961, 1962 or 1963?

CARRY ON SPYING

481. True or false: actor Victor Maddern played the role of Milchmann in this film?

482. What was the name of Barbara Windsor's character in this film?

483. Which of the following actors did not appear in this film - Kenneth Williams, Kenneth Connor or Charles Hawtrey?

484. What was the name of the song composed by Eric Rogers which actress Dilys Laye sings in this film?

485. True or false: actor Bernard Cribbins plays the role of Carstairs in this film?

486. What was the name of the actress who played the role of Dr Crow in this film?

487. How many days did this film take to shoot - 34, 35 or 36?

488. In what year was this film released?

489. Which writer co-wrote the screenplay for this film - Norman Hudis, Sid Colin or Dave Freeman?

490. Kenneth Williams used a character voice in this film that he first used in which BBC radio comedy series?

CARRY ON PERFORMERS ON RECORD

491. True or false: Jim Dale once recorded a song called *Be My Girl*?

492. Which of the following songs did Sid James not record - *Our House, Kids* or *She Was*?

493. Which of the following *Carry On* stars recorded a sketch called 'Good Day to You Sir' - Kenneth Cope and Lance Percival, Kenneth Williams and Lance Percival, or Sid James and Kenneth Connor?

494. Complete the name of the song that Joan Sims recorded: _____ *Song*.

495. Which *Carry On* actress recorded her version of the song *On Mother Kelly's Doorstep* - Dora Bryan, Barbara Windsor or Joan Sims?

496. *Carry On* actor Peter Gilmore once implored us to do what in a song that he recorded - 'Put on a Happy Face', 'Put on a Hat' or 'Put on a Funny Voice'?

497. True or false: Anita Harris once recorded the song *Jane Belinda*?

498. Which of the following songs did Frankie Howerd and Kenneth Connor record together - *Lovely, Second Hand* or *Pennies From Heaven*?

499. True or false: Lance Percival once recorded a song called *The Maharajah of Brum*?

500. What was the title of the song that Frankie Howerd once recorded that was also the name of his highly successful BBC sitcom?

CARRY ON UP THE KHYBER

501. Which actor played Major Shorthouse?

502. True or false: Roy Castle played Captain Keene?

503. In what year was the film released?

504. Which character was played by Joan Sims?

505. Was this the 10th, 13th or 16th *Carry On* film?

506. What was the poster tag-line for this film?

507. True or false: Hattie Jacques played one of the Khasi's wives?

508. Which character did Terry Scott play?

509. Which actress played Busti in the film?

510. Who drew the title sketches used at the start of this film?

MATCH THE FILM - 1

Match up the role played with the correct film

511. Johnny Briggs plays
Sporran Soldier

Carry On Sergeant

512. Richard O'Sullivan plays
Robin Stevens

Carry On Jack

513. Gerald Campion plays
Andy Galloway

Carry On Regardless

514. Jill Ireland plays
Jill Thompson

Carry On Camping

515. Kenneth Williams plays
Francis Courtenay

Carry On Up The Khyber

516. Dorothea Phillips plays
Aunt Beatrice Grubb

Carry On Teacher

517. Ed Devereaux plays
Hook

Carry On Nurse

518. Bill Owen plays
Corporal Bill Copping

Carry On Girls

519. Valerie Leon plays
Paula Perkins

Carry On Loving

520. Betty Marsden plays
Harriet Potter

Carry On Sergeant

CARRY ON CAMPING

521. In which year was this film released in colour?

522. Can you name the two characters that had girlfriends called Anthea and Joan?

523. Following on from the previous question, can you name the two male actors?

524. What was the name of the campsite in the film, which was supposibly located in Devon?

525. Which character did Terry Scott play?

526. True or false: Julian Holloway played Jim Tanner?

527. Which actor played Charlie Muggins in this film?

528. Which finishing school were Dr Kenneth Soaper and his students from?

529. How did the Potters arrive at the campsite - by lorry, by tandem or by car?

530. Which character did Hattie Jacques play?

CARRY ON UP THE JUNGLE

531.　Which character was played by Bernard Bresslaw?

532.　Which actor played Professor Inigo Tinkle?

533.　In which year was this film released in colour?

534.　Which 'Jacki' played June in the film?

535.　What was the name of the all-female tribe?

536.　Which actor played Bill Boosey's assistant?

537.　Was this the 17th, 19th or 21st *Carry On* film?

538.　Which actor played the Witch Doctor in this film?

539.　Which character was played by Joan Sims?

540.　Who played the gorilla in this film?

VALERIE LEON

541. In how many *Carry On* films did Valerie appear - 2, 4 or 6?

542. What was Valerie's first *Carry On* film?

543. True or false: Valerie appeared in *Carry On Camping* as a store assistant?

544. Valerie was born in London, in what year - 1940, 1945 or 1950?

545. Can you name the two James Bond films that Valerie has appeared in?

546. What was the name of Valerie's character in *Carry On Matron*?

547. True or false: Valerie appeared in the film *The Italian Job*?

548. Which *Carry On* film was Valerie appearing in when she played Leda?

549. Following on from the previous question, how much was Valerie paid for her role in the film - £600, £800 or £1,000?

550. Which *Carry On* film was Valerie's last to date?

CARRY ON LAUGHING WITH THE SLIMMING FACTORY

551. Which *Golden Shot* hostess appeared in this stage farce?

552. Which seaside theatre did this stage farce reopen after a period of closure?

553. Who wrote this stage farce?

554. Which *Carry On* actor played the role of Willie Strokes in this farce - Peter Butterworth, Kenneth Connor or Bernard Bresslaw?

555. How many performances of this farce did the cast appear in per week?

556. Actress Linda Hooks played the role of Hilde in this stage show, but how many *Carry On* films did she appear in?

557. Which of the following people was the main designer on this production - Saxon Lucas, John Palmer or Sue Smith?

558. On what date in June 1976 did this stage farce open?

559. How many acts were there to this farce?

560. True or false: actor Danny O'Dea played the role of Albert Waterman in this farce?

JACKI PIPER

561. True or false: Jacki appeared in the film *Carry On Henry*?

562. Jacki played a hospital sister in which *Carry On* film?

563. In which city in the West Midlands was Jacki born?

564. Jacki appeared in which non-*Carry On* film, which starred actor Roger Moore?

565. On what date is Jacki's birthday?

566. True or false: Jacki played the role of Lynne Cox in the Thames TV series, *The Bill*?

567. What was the name of Jacki's character in *Carry On At Your Convenience*?

568. In which of the *Doctor* film series did Jacki briefly appear?

569. What did Jacki's character do when she entered Sid James's character's tent in *Carry On Up the Jungle*?

570. True or false: Jacki appeared opposite fellow *Carry On* actor Terry Scott in the LWT sitcom, *No, Honestly*?

CARRY ON SCREAMING

571. Which star of the BBC sitcom *Steptoe & Son* appears in this film?

572. Which certificate was this film originally granted?

573. When was this film originally released - August 1966, September 1966 or October 1966?

574. Which of the following *Carry On* actors did not appear in this film - Sid James, Kenneth Williams or Charles Hawtrey?

575. What title was this film given in some cinemas when it was shown abroad?

576. Which future *Are You Being Served?* actor appeared in this film - Trevor Bannister, Frank Thornton or Nicholas Smith?

577. True or false: one-time *Doctor Who* actor Jon Pertwee appears in this film?

578. Which veteran *Carry On* actress played the role of Emily Bung in this film?

579. What is the running time of this film?

580. True or false, the lyrics for the song *Carry On Screaming* were written by Talbot Rothwell?

ANGELA DOUGLAS

581. What was the name of the very first *Carry On* film that Angela appeared in?

582. True of false: Angela played the role of Princess Jelhi in the film *Carry On Up the Kyber*?

583. What was the non-*Carry On* film that Angela starred in with fellow *Carry On* actor Jim Dale in 1973?

584. In how many *Carry On* films has Angela appeared to date - 2, 3 or 4?

585. Where was Angela born?

586. True or false: Angela appeared in a film called *It's All Happening*?

587. What is the name of the song that Angela sings in the film *Carry On Cowboy*?

588. True or false: Angela's birthday is on 19 October?

589. What was the name of Angela's character in the film *Carry On Cowboy* - Minnie, Polly or Annie?

590. Which of the following films did Angela not appear in - *Some People*, *The Boys in Blue* or *The Comedy Man*?

SALLY GEESON

591. Name the long-running sitcom that Sally appeared in with Sid James.

592. What was the name of Sally's character in the film *Carry On Abroad?*

593. True or false: Sally once appeared in a film called *What's Good for the Goose*, which starred Norman Wisdom?

594. What was the occupation of Sally's character in the film *Carry On Girls?*

595. Name Sally's actress sister, who appeared in the film *Carry On England.*

596. True or false: Sally appeared in the film *Carry On Dick?*

597. Sally's best friend and travelling companion in *Carry On Abroad* was played by which actress?

598. True or false: Sally took part in the audio commentary for the DVD release of *Carry On Girls?*

599. Sally's character lost which item of clothing in one of the scenes in the film *Carry On Abroad?*

600. True or false: Sally did not appear in any of the *Carry On* TV spin-off specials?

CHARLES HAWTREY

601. True or false: Charles appeared in the first ever *Carry On* film, playing character Peter Golighty?

602. Which *Carry On* film was Charles in when he played Charlie Coote?

603. In what year was Charles born in Middlesex - 1904, 1914 or 1924?

604. Which *Carry On* film was Charles's last, shown in 1972?

605. Which two co-stars were paid more money than Charles when he made his first *Carry On* appearance?

606. Which character did Charles play in *Carry On Loving*?

607. True or false: Charles played character Dan Dann in *Carry On Screaming*?

608. In which year did Charles sadly pass away?

609. True or false: Charles appeared in the ITV sitcom *The Army Game*?

610. How much money did Charles Hawtrey get paid for appearing in *Carry On Cabby* - £2,000, £3,000 or £4,000?

PATSY ROWLANDS

611. In how many *Carry On* films did Patsy appear - 7, 9 or 11?

612. Which *Carry On* film was Patsy's first?

613. In which *Carry On* film was Patsy appearing when she played the character Miss Dempsey?

614. In what year was Patsy born - 1924, 1934 or 1944?

615. In which British sitcom did Patsy play Sid James' neighbour Betty?

616. Which character did Patsy play in *At Your Convenience*?

617. In which *Carry On* film did she play Mildred Bumble?

618. True or false: Patsy played Buxom Lass in the film *Carry On Henry*?

619. In which *Carry On* film did Pasty play Miss Dobbs?

620. Which *Carry On* film was Patsy's last, playing Linda Upmore?

MATCH THE FILM - 2

Match up the role played with the correct film

621.	Carol Hawkins plays Marge	*Carry On Cabby*
622.	Terence Longdon plays Herbert Hall	*Carry On Up The Khyber*
623.	Kenneth Connor plays Major Leep	*Carry On Abroad*
624.	Bernard Bresslaw plays Bunghit Din	*Carry On Nurse*
625.	Joan Sims plays Cora Flange	*Carry On Teacher*
626.	Amanda Barrie plays Cleopatra	*Carry On Constable*
627.	Alexei Sayle plays Aehmed	*Carry On Behind*
628.	Kenneth Connor plays Ted Watson	*Carry On Cleo*
629.	Diana Beevers plays Penny Lee	*Carry On Abroad*
630.	Hilda Fenemore plays Rhoda Bray	*Carry On Columbus*

JOAN SIMS

631. Which *Carry On* film was Joan's first?

632. Following on from the previous question, which character did she play?

633. True or false: Joan appeared in more *Carry On* films than any other actress?

634. Following on from the previous question, in how many *Carry On* films did Joan appear - 22, 24 or 26?

635. In which year was Joan born - 1920, 1925 or 1930?

636. What was the name of the character that Joan played in *Carry On Loving*?

637. Which British sitcom did Joan appear in as Aunt Renee, shown in 1987?

638. In which 1987 children's TV programme did Joan play Lady Fox-Custard?

639. Name the sitcom that Joan starred in with Dennis Waterman and Judy Buxton.

640. In which TV programme did Joan play character Madge Hardcastle, appearing in nine episodes between 1994 and 1998?

CARRY ON ENGLAND

641. In which year was this film released in colour?

642. Which actor played the Brigadier in this film?

643. Who was the best paid actor in the film, receiving £3,000?

644. What was Diane Langton's character name in this film?

645. Was this the 20th, 24th or 28th *Carry On* film?

646. Which character did David Lodge play in the film?

647. Which actor played Gunner Shaw?

648. Which actor played Captain Melly's Driver in the film, the last of his three *Carry On* appearances?

649. Which actor played Captain S. Melly?

650. Which actress played Private Taylor in what was her only *Carry On* film appearance?

CARRY ON THEMES

651. How many times to date has the army been used as a theme in a *Carry On* film?

652. The theme of discovery has to date been used in one *Carry On* film. Can you name it?

653. How many medical-based *Carry On* films have been made to date?

654. Which of the following themes to date has not been used in a *Carry On* film - French Revolution, Monarchy or First World War?

655. True or false: one of the main themes in *Carry On Behind* was archaeology?

656. What was the theme of the edition of the *Carry On Laughing* TV special entitled *The Baron Outlook*?

657. True or false: the theme of the *Carry On* Laughing TV special The Case of the Coughing Parrot was a love story?

658. Which of the following themes was not included in the 1972 Thames TV Christmas special, *Carry On Stuffing* - Victorian melodrama, pantomime or medical?

659. The theme of diplomats was used in which *Carry On* film?

660. True or false: the theme of a 1940s repertory theatre company was used for the stage show *Wot A Carry On In Blackpool*?

CARRY ON FOLLOW THAT CAMEL

661. True or false: actor William Mervyn played the role of Sir Cyril Ponsonby in this film?

662. True or false, the role of Hotel Gentleman in this film was played by an actor called Harold Kasket?

663. True or false: *'Allo 'Allo!* actress Vicki Michelle played one or the Harem Girls in this film?

664. Which *Carry On* actor did not appear in this film - Bernard Bresslaw, Sid James or Charles Hawtrey?

665. Actor Vincent Ball played the part of a ship's officer in this film, but in which previous *Carry On* film had he appeared?

666. Which actress, who later appeared in the film *Carry On Doctor*, played the role of Corktip in this film?

667. What is the name of the café run by Joan Sims's character in this film?

668. To which fort do the Legionnaires march during the film to defend it from attack?

669. True or false: this film is set in 1906?

670. Name the fictitious prophet in the film who decreed that all Legionnaires must die.

BERNARD CRIBBINS

671. In how many *Carry On* films has Bernard appeared to date?

672. Can you name Bernard's first *Carry On* film?

673. Name the hugely popular Wimbledon Common-based children's show that Bernard narrated.

674. True or false: Bernard appeared alongside fellow *Carry On* film star Barbara Windsor in a comedy film called *Crooks in Cloisters*?

675. Name the West End musical that Bernard starred in opposite Elaine Paige at the Prince Edward Theatre.

676. Name Bernard's character in the film *The Railway Children*.

677. Complete the title of the song that was a huge success for Bernard: *Right ____ ____.*

678. On what date does Bernard celebrate his birthday - 28 December, 29 December or 30 December?

679. Name the film musical that Bernard made at ABPC with Tommy Steele and *Carry On* star Sid James.

680. Bernard was a popular storyteller on which children's TV show?

LIZ FRASER

681. What is Liz's full real name?

682. Name the popular TV sitcom which Liz made
      occasional appearances in with Tony Hancock and Sid
      James?

683. True or false: Liz appeared in the film *Confessions of a
      Window Cleaner* with Robin Askwith?

684. Can you name Liz's character in the 1980s Channel 4
      sitcom, *Fairly Secret Army*?

685. Complete the name of the non-*Carry On* film that Liz
      appeared in alongside *Carry On* actor Sid James:
      Double ____.

686. True or false: Liz appeared in the 1967 film *Up the
      Junction*?

687. What was the occupation of Liz's character in her third
      Carry On film - canteen assistant, cleaner or secretary?

688. What was the name of Liz's character in her last *Carry
      On* film to date?

689. How many years' gap was there between Liz's third
      and fourth *Carry On* films?

690. True or false: Liz appeared in the stage show *Carry On
      London*?

DILYS LAYE

691. What was the name of Dilys's character in the film *Carry On Spying*?

692. Which of the following *Carry On* films did Dilys not appear in - *Carry On Doctor, Carry On Camping* or *Carry On Again Doctor*?

693. True or false: Dilys once appeared on Broadway in a production of the musical *The Boyfriend*?

694. What was the name of the TV sitcom that Dilys appeared in alongside actress Sheila Hancock?

695. True or false: Dilys had a small role in the film *Carry On Columbus*, which did not make it into the final cut?

696. Which of the following character names did Dilys not play in a *Carry On* film - Mavis, Anthea or Pat?

697. True or false: Dilys once appeared in a play in London called *Say Who You Are*?

698. Which item of clothing did Dilys claim started to shrink when she was filming scenes in which she and the others became soaked in *Carry On Camping*?

699. Who played Dilys's love interest in *Carry On Doctor*?

700. True or false: Dilys's occupation was a typist in the film *Carry On Cruising*?

CARRY ON DON'T LOSE YOUR HEAD

701. In what year was the film released in colour?

702. Which actress played Desiree Dubarry?

703. True or false: Jim Dale played Lord Darcy de Pue?

704. Was this the 11th, 12th or 13th *Carry On* film?

705. Which actor played the wig-maker Henri?

706. Which actor played Citizen Bidet?

707. Citizen Camembert (Kenneth Williams) was sent to England to find which character in the film?

708. Which actor played Robespierre?

709. Marianne Stone played the landlady in this film, but in how many other *Carry On* films did she appear?

710. Sid James and Kenneth Williams were paid the highest fee for appearing in the film, but how much did they each receive - £3,000, £4,000 or £5,000?

ACTORS - 1

711. Which actor was born in 1925 and played a drunk in *Carry On Cruising*?

712. Which actor, who sadly passed away in 1976, played a waiter in *Carry On Again Doctor*?

713. Which *Carry On* actor's middle name was Alick?

714. Which actor, who was born in 1896 and passed away in 1984, played Alderman Pratt in *Carry On Girls*?

715. Which 'Jon' appeared in four *Carry On* films and sadly died in 1996?

716. Which future *Sale of the Century* presenter played Wolf in *Carry On Regardless*?

717. Which stunt artist played Footpad in *Carry On Dick*?

718. Which actor said, "I think we will Carry On 'til we drop, but it will have been a giggle - for everybody"?

719. Which actor, born in 1937, played Doctor in *Carry On Emmannuelle*?

720. Which actor, who died in 1984, played Agrippa in *Carry On Cleo*?

BERNARD BRESSLAW

721. Which *Carry On* film was Bernard's first?

722. In which comedy series did Bernard play character Private Popplewell?

723. Which *Carry On* film was Bernard's last, playing Arthur Upmore?

724. In which year was Bernard born in London - 1924, 1934 or 1944?

725. What was the name of Bernard's character in *Carry On At Your Convenience*?

726. In how many *Carry On* films did Bernard appear - 7, 14 or 21?

727. What was the second *Carry On* film that Bernard appeared in, shown in 1966?

728. What was the name of Bernard's character in *Carry On Dick*?

729. How much was Bernard paid for his appearance in *Carry On Girls*?

730. What was the name of Bernard's character in *Carry On Doctor*?

CARRY ON LOVING

731. What was Bertram Muffet's profession?

732. Which actor played a marriage guidance counsellor called Percival Snooper?

733. Which actress played Jenny Grubb?

734. What was the name of the dating agency owned by Sidney and Sophie?

735. From what did Bertrum Muffet make aeroplanes?

736. Which two actors earned the most money for appearing in the film, receiving £5,000 each?

737. Which actress played the model Sally Martin?

738. In which year was the film released?

739. Which actress played Mrs Dreery in this film?

740. Can you name the *Carry On* film that was made after *Carry On Loving*?

LESLIE PHILLIPS

741. In how many *Carry On* films has Leslie appeared - 2, 4 or 6?

742. True or false: Leslie Phillips appeared in the Steve Coogan film *The Parole Officer*?

743. In which film, also starring Angelina Jolie, did Leslie play Wilson in 2001?

744. What was the name of Leslie's character in *Carry On Teacher*?

745. In which 2007 film did Leslie play Ian, a role for which he was nominated for a BAFTA award?

746. In which year was Leslie born - 1918, 1924 or 1930?

747. How much was Leslie paid for appearing in *Carry On Nurse*?

748. In which *Carry On* film did Leslie play the King of Spain?

749. What was Leslie awarded in 1998 for his services to drama?

750. Can you name the 1994 comedy serial in which Leslie played Lord Flanborough?

ROBIN ASKWITH

751. Robin appeared in which *Carry On* film?

752. True or false: Robin played Mike in the sitcom film spin-off of *Bless this House*?

753. In how many *Confessions* films did Robin appear?

754. True or false: Robin once appeared in an episode of the sitcom *Please, Sir!*?

755. In which Terry Johnson play did Robin tour during 2007?

756. What is the name of Robin's autobiography?

757. Name the ITV sitcom in which Robin played a milkman.

758. True or false: Robin appeared in one of the *Carry On* TV spin-off specials?

759. Name the Yorkshire TV sitcom in which Robin played the role of Harvey C in Series 2.

760. True or false: Robin played Mike's friend in the TV version of *Bless this House*?

CARRY ON CATCHPHRASES

761. What was the well-known catchphrase that Charles Hawtrey usually spoke on his first appearance in each *Carry On* film?

762. Which catchphrase did Kenneth Williams often use in the *Carry On* films, which he first used back in the *Hancock's Half Hour* days?

763. Bernard Bresslaw often used a catchphrase in the *Carry On* films that he first used in the TV sitcom series, *The Army Game*, but what was it?

764. Which of the following catchphrases did Sid James often use in the *Carry On* films - "Cor blimey!", "Cor missus!" or "Cor matron!"?

765. Leslie Phillips will be forever remembered for saying "Hello!" in the *Carry On* films, but which other catchphrase did he use in the film *Carry On Nurse*?

766. What was Kenneth Williams' best-known catchphrase from the film *Carry On Screaming*?

767. Kenneth Williams will be forever remembered for which catchphrase in the medical-themed *Carry On* films?

768. True or false: Warren Mitchell used his *Till Death Us Do Part* catchphrase, "You silly moo", in the film *Carry On Cleo*?

769. Peter Butterworth's character Josh Fiddler had a one-word catchphrase in *Carry On Camping*. What was it?

770. Name Kenneth Williams's memorable catchphrase from the film *Carry On Cleo*.

CARRY ON SCRIPTWRITERS

771. How many *Carry On* films did Talbot Rothwell write?

772. True or false: Barry Cryer contributed material to the film *Carry on England*?

773. Name the two *Carry On* films that Dave Freeman wrote.

774. Which co-writer of the radio show *Beyond Our Ken* wrote some of the material for the stage show *Carry On London*?

775. True or false: Tony Hawes was the programme associate on the TV version of *What A Carry On!* hosted by Shaw Taylor?

776. Which of the following writers contributed extra material to the script of *Carry On Columbus* - Barry Cryer, John Antrobus or Dick Vosburgh?

777. Who wrote the *Carry On Laughing* TV special entitled *One in the Eye for Harold*?

778. True or false: *Carry On* writer Dave Freeman also wrote the screenplay for the film spin-off to the sitcom *Bless this House*?

779. Which of the following writers contributed extra material to the stage show *Carry On London* - Ian Grant, Vince Powell or Lance Peters?

780. True or false: the writers of *Carry On England*, David Pursall and Jack Sneddon, also wrote an unmade *Carry On* screenplay with the theatre as its theme?

CARRY ON
CHARACTER NAMES

781. True or false: the name of Kenneth Williams' character in *Carry On Behind* was Professor Roland Crump?

782. What was the name of Jim Dale's character in *Carry On Screaming*?

783. Nurse Willing was Elizabeth Knight's character in which *Carry On* film?

784. Name the character played by actress Prudence Soloman in the film *Carry On Columbus*?

785. What was Diana Darvey's character name in *Carry On Behind*?

786. Can you name the actress who played Busti in the film *Carry On Up the Kyber*?

787. Can you name Amelia Bayntun's character in *Carry On at Your Convenience*?

788. Which of the following character names did Barbara Windsor not have in the *Carry On* film - Nurse Susan Ball, Sadie Tomkins or Linda Upmore?

789. Big Heap was Charles Hawtrey's character in which *Carry On* film?

790. Mrs Tuttle was played by which actress in *Carry On Abroad*?

RICHARD O'SULLIVAN

791. Name the *Carry On Emmannuelle* actress which Richard appeared alongside in the 1972 sitcom, *Alcock & Gander*?

792. Name the *Man About the House* sitcom spin-off that Richard starred in and whose character co-ran a small bistro.

793. Richard played a father in which LWT sitcom in the mid-to-late '80s?

794. True or false: Richard filmed two scenes for the film *Carry On Behind* which were later cut?

795. On what date does Richard celebrate his birthday?

796. Which of the following TV series did Richard not appear in - *Doctor at Large*, *Dick Turpin* or *French Fields*?

797. True or false: Richard appeared in the West End of London in the farce *Run for Your Wife*?

798. Can you name the Cliff Richard film that Richard appeared in?

799. What was the name of the Ronnie Barker film that Richard appeared in?

800. How old was Richard when he played the lead role in a TV version of *Little Lord Fauntleroy* - 11, 12 or 13?

CARRY ON MATRON

801. Which actor played a twitching father?

802. Who played Sir Bernard Cutting, the chief surgeon?

803. In what year was this film released in colour?

804. Which actor played Cyril, Sid Carter's son, who dressed up as a nurse?

805. True or false: actress Zena Clifton plays the Au Pair Girl in this film?

806. Which actress played Matron?

807. True or false: Bill Maynard played Freddy?

808. Which other *Carry On* film was released in the same year as *Carry On Matron*?

809. What was the name of the maternity hospital?

810. Which character did actress Gwendolyn Watts play?

ACTRESSES - 1

811. Which actress played Mrs Parker in *Carry On Screaming*?

812. Which actress played Dolores in *Carry On Cowboy*, her only *Carry On* appearance?

813. In which two *Carry On* films did actress Georgina Moon appear?

814. Which *On the Buses* actress appeared in *Carry On Camping* and *Carry On Loving*?

815. Which actress, who was born in 1909 and passed away in 1999, played Mrs Beasley in *Carry On Again Doctor*?

816. Which actress, born in 1912, featured in three *Carry On* films, including playing Dr Crow in *Carry On Spying*?

817. Which actress, born in Malaysia, featured in *Carry On Again Doctor* and *Carry On Up the Jungle*?

818. Which actress played the role of Norma Baxter in *Carry On Behind*?

819. Which actress played Pretty Bidder in *Carry On Cleo* and Khasi's Wife in *Carry On Up the Khyber*?

820. Which actress played an aristocratic lady in *Carry On Cabby*?

CARRY ON COWBOY

821. Which actor played the Rumpo Kid?

822. True or false: Kenneth Williams played Judge Burke in this film?

823. In which year was the film released in colour?

824. Which two actors were paid £5,000 each for appearing in the film?

825. Which *Carry On* film was released after this film?

826. Which actress played Annie Oakley?

827. True or false: Margaret Nolan played Miss Jones?

828. What was the name of the Western town in which the story was set?

829. Which actor played Marshall P. Knutt?

830. True or false: the dancing girls in this film were from the Ballet Montparnasse?

KENNETH WILLIAMS

831. What was Kenneth's first *Carry On* film?

832. Following on from the previous question, what was his character's name?

833. In how many *Carry On* films did Kenneth appear?

834. What was the name of Kenneth's character in *Carry On Emmannuelle*?

835. In which *Carry On* film did Kenneth play Desmond Simpkins?

836. Complete the name of the BBC TV show that Kenneth once hosted: *International* _____.

837. What is Kenneth's most used catchphrase?

838. Kenneth was paid a higher fee than any other actor in *Carry On Up the Khyber*, but how much did he receive?

839. In which *Carry On* film did Kenneth play Commandant Burger?

840. How old was Kenneth when he sadly passed away in 1988?

FRANKIE HOWERD

841. In how many *Carry On* films did Frankie appear - 2, 4 or 6?

842. Can you name all the *Carry On* films that Frankie appeared in?

843. What was the name of Frankie's character in his first *Carry On* film?

844. What was Frankie awarded by the Queen in 1977?

845. In which film, shown in 1966, did Frankie appear with Reg Varney and Dora Bryan?

846. In which 1963 film did Frankie appear with Ron Moody, Terry Thomas and Margaret Rutherford?

847. True or false: Frankie used to sing a song in his act called *Three Little Fishes*?

848. In which film did Frankie make his screen debut, playing opposite Petula Clark?

849. In which year was Frankie born - 1907, 1917 or 1927?

850. Frankie sadly died before the filming of which *Carry On* film that he was scheduled to appear in?

SHIRLEY EATON

851. In which *Carry On* film does Leslie Phillips' character calm Shirley's character's pre-wedding nerves?

852. Shirley was once in a stage act at the London Palladium with which veteran British entertainer?

853. Name the Bond film that Shirley appeared in.

854. Shirley originally retired from acting in which year?

855. True or false: Shirley was interviewed in the TV documentary *What's A Carry On?*?

856. Which of the following *Carry On* films did Shirley not appear in - *Carry On Nurse*, *Carry On Constable* or *Carry On Regardless*?

857. True or false: Shirley appeared in the film *Dentist in the Chair*?

858. What is the name of Shirley's character's fiancé in her third *Carry On* film?

859. What does Shirley's character end up working as in her first *Carry On* film?

860. True or false: Shirley played Arthur Askey's daughter in a film called *The Love Match*?

CARRY ON AT PINEWOOD STUDIOS

861. To date, how many different stages has it taken in total to make the *Carry On* films at Pinewood Studios?

862. Which well-known actor unveiled a plaque at Pinewood Studios to commemorate fifty years since Peter Rogers first began working at the studios?

863. True or false: the gardens at Pinewood Studios were used for shooting certain scenes in the film *Carry On Henry*?

864. Whereabouts at Pinewood Studios are the buildings used for shooting several scenes set in a lavatory-making factory in *Carry On At Your Convenience*?

865. The rear of the mansion house at Pinewood Studios was used for the making of which of the following *Carry On* films - *Carry On Sergeant*, *Carry On Nurse* or *Carry On Doctor*?

866. True or false: to date none of the *Carry On* TV spin-off specials has ever been made at Pinewood Studios?

867. Which part of Pinewood Studios was used in the opening sequence in the film *Carry On Spying*?

868. Which of the following stages at Pinewood Studios were used for the shooting of the film *Carry On Cabby* - A and C, B and C, or C and D?

869. What is the name of the lady who for many years acted as Peter Rogers' PA at Pinewood Studios - Audrey Skinner, Yvonne Caffin or Jane Buck?

870. True or false: the orchard at Pinewood Studios was used for filming certain scenes in the film *Carry On Screaming*?

CARRY ON
BEHIND THE CAMERA

871. True or false: Ernest Steward was the director of photography on 10 *Carry On* films?

872. Which of the following women worked as a hairdresser on 21 of the *Carry On* films - Stella Rivers, Biddy Crystal or Sue Love?

873. Dave Bracknell, who was one of the assistant directors on the *Carry On* films, had a daughter who became an actress and went on to appear in the soap *Emmerdale*. What is her name?

874. True or false: Geoffrey Rodway worked as a make-up artist on 26 *Carry On* films?

875. Which camera operator on the *Carry On* films also worked as a director of photography on 16 of the films?

876. Which of the following people did not work on a *Carry On* film as a costume designer - Anna Duse, Julie Harris or Gina Jay?

877. How many *Carry On* films did Alfred Roome edit?

878. True or false: Penny Daniels worked on continuity on six *Carry On* films?

879. Which of the following men did not work as an art director on a *Carry On* film - Cedric Dawe, Peter Childs or Bert Batt?

880. Who wrote and produced the end title song for the film *Carry On Columbus*?

CARRY ON
CAST BIRTHDAYS

881. Kenneth Connor was born on 6 June, but in which year?

882. Where was Charles Hawtrey born in November 1934?

883. On what date is Jim Dale's birthday - 15 July, 15 August or 15 September?

884. Jack Douglas was born in Newcastle on which date in April 1927?

885. True or false: Bernard Bresslaw's birthday was on 25 February?

886. Joan Sims was born on which date in May 1930?

887. Terry Scott was born in Watford on 4 May in which year?

888. In which year was *Carry On Up the Kyber* actor Cardew Robinson born?

889. Peter Butterworth was born in Bramhall on 4 February, but in which year?

890. Which *Carry On* team actress celebrated her birthday on 19 January?

JUNE WHITFIELD

891. Which of the following films did June not appear in - *Carry On Girls, Carry On Behind* or *Carry On Columbus?*

892. June appeared in which sitcom spin-off film made by Peter Rogers and Gerald Thomas?

893. What was the name of June's character in the BBC radio series *Take It From Here?*

894. True or false: June was awarded the OBE in 1985?

895. Can you name June's actress daughter?

896. True or false: June appeared in an episode of Julian Clary's Channel 4 sitcom, *Terry & Julian?*

897. In which long-running BBC Radio 2 series did June star alongside Roy Hudd?

898. On what date does June celebrate her birthday - 11 November, 12 November or 13 November?

899. June appeared as a nurse in which edition of the TV sitcom *Hancock?*

900. True or false: June once appeared in a film called *The Spy with the Cold Nose?*

ACTRESSES - 2

901. Which actress played a bird keeper in the film *Carry On Regardless?*

902. Which actress was born in 1919 and played Madame Fifi in *Carry On Abroad?*

903. Which actress played the Amazon Guard in *Carry On Spying* and Hand Maiden in *Carry On Cleo?*

904. Which actress played Mrs Smith in *Carry On Doctor* and later appeared in *Dad's Army?*

905. Which actress appeared in two films, *Carry On England* and *Carry On Emmannuelle*, and also appeared in *The Dick Emery Show?*

906. Which actress played Private Murray in *Carry On England* and Nurse in *Carry On Emmannuelle?*

907. Which actress, born in 1911, appeared in *Carry On Don't Lose Your Head* and *Carry On Again Doctor*, and sadly died in 1999?

908. Which actress was paid £2,500 for appearing in *Carry On Up The Khyber?*

909. Which well-known actress, born on the Isle of Wight in 1933, played Senna Pod in *Carry On Cleo?*

910. Which actress played Katherine Howard in *Carry On Henry?*

CARRY ON CLEO

911. Which future *Coronation Street* actress played Cleopatra?

912. In which year was the film released?

913. What was the tag-line for this film?

914. Which actor played Julius Caesar?

915. Which two actors were paid £5,000 each for their appearances?

916. Which actress played Calpurnia?

917. Was this the 7th, 9th or 11th *Carry On* film?

918. Which other *Carry On* film was released in the same year?

919. Which actor played Sergeant Major?

920. Which character sent Mark Anthony, played by Sid James, to see Cleopatra?

MATCH THE DATE - 4

Match up the event with the date it happened

921.	Joy Harrington was born	1998
922.	The first *Carry On Christmas* was shown	1975
923.	Richard O'Brien was born	1989
924.	The *Carry On Laughing* series started	1929
925.	The first *Carry On* film was released	1969
926.	Wendy Richard was born	1914
927.	Henry Livings sadly passed away	1942
928.	*Carry On Camping* was released	1946
929.	Joe Robinson was born	1958
930.	Jack Shampan sadly passed away	1969

CARRY ON AT YOUR CONVENIENCE

931.   In what year was the film released - 1967, 1969 or 1971?

932.   Which actor played W. C. Boggs?

933.   Name the actor who played the hotel manager in this film.

934.   Name the character who was the union representative.

935.   Which actor played Lewis Boggs, the boss's son?

936.   What was the name of Sid Plummer's pet budgie, which won him money on the races?

937.   Where was the firm's outing to - Clacton on Sea, Southend on Sea or Brighton?

938.   In what year was the company W. C. Boggs and Sons established?

939.   Which actress played Chloe Moore?

940.   Which other *Carry On* film was released in the same year?

ACTORS - 2

941. Which actor, who was born in 1918 and sadly passed away in 1996, played the Spanish Governor in *Carry On Jack*?

942. Which actor played Major Carstairs in *Carry On England*?

943. Which actor played Man in the Laundrette in *Carry On Emmannuelle*?

944. Which actor, born in 1930, played Eric in *Carry On Constable* and Leonard Beamish in *Carry On Regardless*?

945. Which actor, born in Scotland in 1936, played Trapper in *Carry On Cowboy* and Highwayman in *Carry On Dick*?

946. Which actor played Nick in *Carry On Nurse*, Sam in *Carry On Doctor* and Porter in *Carry On Again Doctor*?

947. Which actor played Gunner Shaw in *Carry On England*?

948. Which actor played William Wakefield in *Carry On Teacher*?

949. Which actor appeared in four *Carry On* films, including playing Smiley in *Carry On Cabby* and Percy Hickson in *Carry On Nurse*?

950. Which actor played a chaplain in *Carry On Doctor*?

POT LUCK - 3

951. True or false: *Carry On* film director Gerald Thomas provided the voice for the foul-mouthed mynah bird in the film *Carry On Behind*?

952. What was the working title for the film *Carry On Up the Jungle*?

953. What was the name of the actress who played Jacqueline in *Carry On Don't Lose Your Head*?

954. What was the name of Valerie Leon's character in *Carry On Girls* - Paula Perkins, Dawn Brakes or Ida Downs?

955. Shakira Baksh appeared as the slender version of a character called Scrubba in *Carry On Up the Jungle*, but which film actor did this actress marry in real life?

956. What was the name of the future *Last of the Summer Wine* actor who played the man from Cox & Carter's in the film *Carry On Doctor*?

957. Which of the following actors played the role of the bus conductor at the start of the film *Carry On Loving* - Melvyn Hayes, Kenny Lynch or Julian Holloway?

958. What is the name of the actress who played the role of Willa Claudia in the film *Carry On Cleo*?

959. Name the actress who appeared on stage with Sid James in the farce *The Mating Season*, and who also appeared in the film *Carry On Abroad* as Madame Fifi.

960. What does Joan Sims fall against in a scene that takes place in the hotel lobby in *Carry On Girls*?

CARRY ON BOOKS

961. *What a Carry On - The Official Story of the Carry On Film Series* by Sally Hibbin and Nina Hibbin was first published in which year - 1987, 1988 or 1989?

962. True or false: the book *Carry On Laughing - A Celebration* was written by Cliff Goodwin?

963. Joan Sims recalled working on the *Carry On* films in her autobiography first published in 2000, but what was the name of her book?

964. *The Man Who Was Private Widdle* is a biography on Charles Hawtrey, but which of the following authors wrote this book - Paul Burton, Roger Lewis or Chris Cowlin?

965. What is the name of the broadcaster and journalist who edited *The Kenneth Williams Diaries* and *The Kenneth Williams Letters*?

966. What is the name of Robert Ross's biography on Sid James, first published in 2000?

967. True or false: *Carry On* actress June Whitfield's autobiography is called *And This is June Whitfield*?

968. *A Twitch in Time* is the autobiography of which *Carry On* actor?

969. *Mr Carry On: The Life and Work of Peter Rogers* was a book written by which two writers?

970. Kenneth Williams's autobiography *Just Williams* was first published in what year?

BOB MONKHOUSE

971. True or false: Bob appeared in a scene for the film *Carry On Nurse*, but it was edited out of the final cut?

972. Name the dentist-themed comedy film that Bob starred in with the *Carry On* team members, including Kenneth Connor, Charles Hawtrey and Shirley Eaton.

973. Which actress played Bob's wife in the film *Carry On Sergeant?*

974. What was the name of Bob's character in *Carry On Sergeant?*

975. True or false: Bob provided additional material for the film *Carry On Regardless?*

976. Name the TV talent show that Bob presented on BBC1 in the 1980s.

977. Which of the following quiz shows did Bob not present on TV - *Celebrity Squares, The Golden Shot* or *Every Second Counts?*

978. Name the bingo-themed TV quiz show that Bob hosted on BBC1.

979. What was the name of Bob's first autobiography, published in 1993?

980. True or false: Bob appeared in a TV show recorded in England for American TV called *Bonkers?*

POT LUCK - 4

981. Name the actress whose character witnesses the early-morning showering activities of Kenneth Williams in a a scene in *Carry On Constable*.

982. Which 'Singers' performed the song at the start of *Carry On Don't Lose Your Head*?

983. True or false: Patsy Rowlands plays the small role of one of Henry VIII's wives at the start of the film *Carry On Henry*?

984. Which of the following actors played Mr Bulstrode in the film *Carry On At Your Convenience* - Geoffrey Hughes, Philip Stone or Davy Kaye?

985. True or false: singer Lily Allen's father, Keith, appeared in the film *Carry On Columbus*?

986. Which future *Emmerdale* actress plays a Bunny Girl in *Carry On At Your Convenience*?

987. What is the first name of John Clive's character in the film *Carry On Abroad*?

988. True or false: the original idea for the film *Carry On Cabby* came from S. C. Green and Dick Hills, one-time writers of *The Morecambe & Wise Show*?

989. Name the successful BBC1 sitcom that Kenneth Waller, who played the barman in *Carry On Behind*, later starred in as Grandad.

990. Name the actor turned theatre producer who played the role of the newspaper reporter in *Carry On Matron*.

ERIC ROGERS

991. What age was Eric when he first began his music tuition?

992. For which popular West End musical, also turned into a film musical, did Eric make the music arrangements?

992. For which popular Sunday night TV show did Eric write the theme tune?

993. For how many *Carry On* films did Eric compose and conduct the music - 18, 22 or 26?

995. True or false: Eric was also a TV scriptwriter?

996. For which London-to-Brighton-themed 1953 comedy film did Eric compose the music?

997. True or false: Eric was writing a book on music when he died in 1977?

998. A few bars of the theme tune of which popular sitcom were included by Eric in the film *Carry On Screaming*, for which he composed and conducted the score?

999. During his RAF days in the Second World War, which instrument did Eric play to earn himself free beer?

1000. True or false: Peter Rogers and Eric Rogers were related?

ANSWERS

SID JAMES

1.   South Africa

2.   Sid Abbott

3.   True

4.   *Hancock's Half Hour*

5.   Sidney Bliss

6.   True: Reine and Laurie James

7.   £2,000

8.   19

9.   *Carry On Dick*

10.   Sid Plummer

CARRY ON AGAIN DOCTOR

11.   1969

12.   Goldie Locks

13.   True

14.   Gerald Thomas

15.   Long Hampton Hospital

16.   Jim Dale

17.   Hattie Jacques

18.   Gladstone Screwer

19.   Patsy Rowlands

20.   False: She played New Matron

BARBARA WINDSOR

21.   9

22.   *Carry On Spying*

23. Daphne Honeybutt

24. London

25. EastEnders

26. Peggy Mitchell

27. The Belles of St Trinian's

28. Carry On Dick

29. Bettina

30. Carry On Doctor

MATCH THE DATE - 1

31.	Sally Douglas was born	1942
32.	Carry On Nurse was released	1959
33.	Carry On Behind was released	1975
34.	Dany Robin sadly passed away	1995
35.	Margaret Nolan was born	1943
36.	Carry On Henry was released	1971
37.	Sid James sadly passed away	1976
38.	Anna Karen was born	1936
39.	Bob Todd sadly passed away	1991
40.	Carry On Columbus was released	1992

CARRY ON ABROAD

41. 1972

42. True

43. Miss Sadie Tomkins

44. Pub landlord

45. Kenneth Williams

46.   *Elsbels Palace Hotel*

47.   *Floella*

48.   *June Whitfield*

49.   *Stanley*

50.   *True*

KENNETH CONNOR

51.   *17*

52.   *Boxer*

53.   *Horace Strong*

54.   *Sheila Hancock*

55.   *Carry On Dick, Carry On Behind* and *Carry On England*

56.   *2*

57.   *A Funny Thing Happened on the Way to the Forum*

58.   *False*

59.   *Dynamite*

60.   *Miss Wheeler*

THAT'S CARRY ON

61.   *In one of the projector rooms at Pinewood Studios*

62.   *Go to the lavatory*

63.   *Carry On England*

64.   *April 1977*

65.   *False: the linking material was written by Tony Church*

66.   *Everyone who's anyone is in it ... Right in it!*

67.   *Eric Rogers*

68.   *'A' certificate*

69.   February 1978

70.   She locks him in the projector room

CARRY ON DICK

71.   Laurie Wyman and George Evans

72.   The Old Cock Inn

73.   Eva Reuber-Staier

74.   Sam Kelly

75.   Sergeant Jock Strapp

76.   Hattie Jacques

77.   The church organ

78.   Margaret Nolan

79.   He was a Bow Street Runner called Captain Desmond Fancey

80.   False

JIM DALE

81.   An expectant father

82.   Sanitary engineer

83.   He tried to put together a jigsaw

84.   Angela Douglas

85.   23

86.   11

87.   False

88.   *Carry On Don't Lose Your Head*

89.   True

90.   *Oliver!*

PETER GILMORE

91. Dancy, a petty gangster

92. False

93. 11

94. A lovely looking pear

95. Galley master

96. True

97. Joan Sims

98. Private Ginger Hale

99. *Carry On Columbus*

100. *Carry On Don't Lose Your Head*

BILL MAYNARD

101. Fred Moore

102. 5

103. *Carry On Loving, Carry On Henry, Carry On At Your Convenience, Carry On Matron, Carry On Dick*

104. *Carry On Henry*

105. Claude Greengrass

106. *Confessions from a Holiday Camp*

107. *The Yo-Yo Man*

108. Butlins (Skegness)

109. 1928

110. *Carry On Abroad*

CARRY ON BEHIND

111. George Layton

112. On a fishing trip

113. 1975

114. River Side

115. Ian Lavendar

116. University of Kidburn

117. Professor Anna Vooshka

118. False: Carol was played by Sherrie Hewson

119. Arthur Upmore

120. Joan Sims

JACK DOUGLAS

121. 8

122. True: he played a character called Jake

123. Twitching

124. *Carry On Matron*

125. True: he played Marco the Cereal Killer

126. A theatre producer

127. Newcastle

128. True

129. *Carry On Girls*

130. True

HATTIE JACQUES

131. *Carry On Sergeant*

132. *Sykes*

133. Sid James

134. Sophie Bliss

108

135. 14

136. 1924

137. *Carry On Cabby*

138. Beattie Plummer

139. John Le Mesurier

140. *Carry On Dick*

CARRY ON COLUMBUS

141. 1992

142. Maureen Lipman

143. False: Fatima was played by Sara Crowe

144. King Ferdinand

145. John Goldstone (Peter Rogers was executive producer)

146. Rik Mayall

147. Martin Clunes

148. True

149. Jim Dale

150. Wang

NORMAN HUDIS

151. He wrote six *Carry On* screenplays that were filmed

152. *Carry On Regardless*

153. True, although it was sadly never made

154. *Carry On Cruising*

155. *Carry On Nurse*

156. *Carry On Jack*

157. *Twice Round the Daffodils*

158. False

159. 1923

160. Slough Police Station

PETER ROGERS

161. True

162. Tommy Steele

163. *Trouble in Store*

164. 1960

165. True

166. Betty E. Box

167. Speedy Gonzales

168. True

169. *Circus Friends*

170. 20 February 1914

POT LUCK - 1

171. *Carry On Cabby*

172. True

173. *Sale of the Century*

174. Professor Inigo Tinkle

175. False: the role was played by Joan Hickson

176. *Carry On Henry*

177. E. V. H. Emmett

178. Gripper Burke

179. 7

180. James Beck

CARRY ON EMMANNUELLE

181. Mrs Dangle

182. Lance Peters

183. True

184. Henry McGee

185. £6,000

186. Suzanne Danielle

187. Kenny Lynch

188. 88 minutes

189. Beryl Reid

190. 'AA' certificate

GERALD THOMAS

191. Denham

192. True

193. 1920

194. Laugh with the Carry Ons

195. True

196. Bless this House

197. All the various scripts and documents connected with the *Carry On* film series

198. The Life of Kenneth Connor

199. Time Lock

200. 1993

MATCH THE DATE - 2

201. *Carry On Cowboy* was released   1965

111

202.	Angela Douglas was born	1940
203.	*Carry On Cleo* was released	1964
204.	George Layton appeared in his only *Carry On* film	1975
205.	*Carry On Loving* was released	1970
206.	Imogen Hassall sadly passed away	1980
207.	Arthur Lovegrove sadly passed away	1981
208.	Thirteen Rank-financed *Carry On* films were released onto video	1987
209.	Bob Monkhouse sadly passed away	2003
210.	Barbara Windsor appeared in the stage show *What a Carry On*	1985

PETER BUTTERWORTH

211. *Carry On Cowboy*

212. Doc

213. 16

214. Josh Fiddler

215. True

216. 1919

217. Janet Brown

218. *Bless this House*

219. Earl of Bristol

220. *Carry On Up the Khyber*

CARRY ON CONSTABLE

221. 1960

222. Shirley Eaton

223. Kenneth Williams

224. 4th

225. Sergeant Frank Wilkins

226. Leslie Phillips

227. All 3: *Carry On Sergeant*, *Carry On Nurse* and *Carry On Teacher*

228. True

229. True

230. WPC Harrison

MATCH THE DATE - 3

231. Barbara Windsor took her one-woman show,

    Carry On Barbara to Australia and New Zealand   1975

232. Bill Cunnings appeared in his only *Carry On* film   1964

233. Harry Locke sadly passed away   1987

234. *Carry On Abroad* was premiered   1978

235. Jerry Desmonde sadly passed away   1967

236. Patricia Hayes appeared in her only *Carry On* film   1969

237. Bill Pertwee appeared in his last *Carry On* film   1973

238. Leigh Madison appeared in her first *Carry On* film   1958

239. Wilfred Bramble was born   1912

240. Toby Dale appeared in his only *Carry On* film to date   1992

TERRY SCOTT

241. *Carry On Sergeant*

242. Paddy O'Brien

243. 1927

244. 7

245. *Carry On Henry*

246. Terence Philpot

247. June Whitfield

248. Dr Prodd

249. True

250. 1994

JULIAN HOLLOWAY

251. Her nightie

252. Major Butcher

253. *Carry On Screaming*

254. True

255. Julian Robert Stanley Holloway

256. 1944

257. 1973

258. True

259. RADA

260. False

CARRY ON SERGEANT

261. Miles Heywood

262. True

263. R. F. Delderfield

264. John Antrobus

265. The Coldstream Guards

266. True

267. Leslie Phillips

268.   £74,000

269.   Six weeks

270.   180

CARRY ON LONDON - THE REVUE

271.   The Birmingham Hippodrome

272.   Kenneth Williams

273.   Albert J. Knight

274.   False: the other writers were Dave Freeman, Eric Merriman and Ian Grant

275.   Victoria Palace

276.   18 months

277.   True

278.   £50,000

279.   ATV

280.   Pete Murray

CARRY ON LAUGHING - TV SERIES

281.   ATV

282.   4

283.   *Outlook*

284.   True

285.   Simon Callow

286.   Bernard Bresslaw

287.   False

288.   13

289.   Kenneth Williams

290. True

CARRY ON NURSE

291. Ring For Catty

292. A nuclear physics student

293. King George V Men's Surgical Ward

294. June Whitfield

295. 86 minutes

296. 'U' certificate

297. Journalist

298. True

299. Joan Sims

300. A daffodil

APPEARANCES

301.	Liz Fraser	4
302.	Donald Hewlett	1
303.	Larry Dann	4
304.	Windsor Davies	2
305.	Derek Francis	6
306.	Ian Curry	2
307.	Julian Holloway	8
308.	Anne Scott	2
309.	Wanda Ventham	2
310.	Richard O'Callaghan	2

CARRY ON CRUISING

311. Sid James

312. 6th

313. Dilys Laye

314. Dr Arthur Binn

315. SS Happy Wanderer

316. Leonard Marjoribanks

317. Shapely Miss

318. False: Glad Trimble was played by Liz Fraser

319. 10

320. False: Bridget Madderley was played by Esma Cannon

LOCATIONS - 1

321.	Maidenhead Town Hall	*Carry On Again Doctor*
322.	Waddesdon Manor, Bucks	*Carry On Don't Lose Your Head*
323.	Beaconsfield Church, Bucks	*Carry On Sergeant*
324.	Beddgelert, Snowdonia North Wales	*Carry On Up the Kyber*
325.	Hanwell Parish Church	*Carry On Constable*
326.	Drayton Secondary School, Drayton Gardens, West Ealing	*Carry On Teacher*
327.	Camber Sands, Rye, Sussex	*Carry On Follow That Camel*
328.	Town Hall, Slough	*Carry On Girls*

| 329. | The Palace Hotel, Brighton | *Carry On At Your Convenience* |
| 330. | Heatherwood Hospital, Ascot, Bucks | *Carry On Matron* |

CARRY ON HENRY

331. 1971

332. Sid James

333. Derek Francis

334. Peter Gilmore

335. Colour

336. True

337. False: the role was played by Alan Curtis

338. True

339. Jane Cardew

340. Thomas Cromwell

MATCH THE CHARACTER - 1

341.	Bob Monkhouse	Charlie Sage (*Carry On Sergeant*)
342.	Patrick Cargill	Spanish Governor (*Carry On Jack*)
343.	Wendy Richard	Ida Downs (*Carry On Girls*)
344.	Charles Hawtrey	Captain Le Pice (*Carry On Follow That Camel*)

345.	Dianna MacNamara	Princess Stephanie (*Carry On Don't Lose Your Head*)
346.	Angela Douglas	Annie Oakley (*Carry On Cowboy*)
347.	Charles Hawtrey	Peter Golightly (*Carry On Sergeant*)
348.	Phil Silvers	Sergeant Ernie Nocker (*Carry On Follow That Camel*)
349.	Eric Baker	Inspector Mills (*Carry On Constable*)
350.	Rosalind Knight	Felicity Wheeler (*Carry On Teacher*)

CARRY ON TEACHER

351. Richard O'Sullivan

352. *Carry On Behind, Carry On England* and *Carry On Emmannuelle*

353. False: the role was played by Cyril Chamberlain

354. Charles Hawtrey

355. Liz Fraser

356. True

357. Edwin Milton

358. August 1959

359. 40

360. Maudlin Street School

CARRY ON CHRISTMAS - TV SPECIALS

361.   Robert Browning and Fairy Godmother

362.   False: the role was played by Kenneth Connor

363.   Sid James

364.   Mr Belcher

365.   True

366.   Virginia

367.   Wendy Richard

368.   50 minutes

369.   True

370.   Genie of the Lamp

WOT A CARRY ON IN BLACKPOOL!

371.   True

372.   Bernard Bresslaw and Barbara Windsor

373.   True

374.   1992

375.   North Pier

376.   False: it was performer Richard Gauntlett

377.   Tudor Davies

378.   True

379.   2

380.   25 October

CARRY ON REGARDLESS

381.   Helping Hands Agency

382.   Fenella Fielding

383. Terence Alexander

384. True

385. "Funniest Carry On Ever!"

386. Hattie Jacques

387. True

388. Freddie Mills

389. Montgomery Infield-Hopping

390. Bill Owen

WHAT'S A CARRY ON?

391. True

392. Kenneth Connor

393. Karl Howman

394. 1998

395. ITV1

396. Peter Butterworth

397. Tom O'Connor

398. Jack Douglas and Patsy Rowlands

399. Norman Hudis

400. Jacki Piper

CARRY ON CABBY

401. Charlie Hawkins

402. Peggy Hawkins

403. Esma Cannon

404. Speedie Taxis

405. Glamcabs

406. Charles Hawtrey

407. Black and white

408. False: she played Anthea

409. Norman Chappell

410. Ford Cortina's

CARRY ON GIRLS

411. Hope Springs

412. Bernard Bresslaw

413. A beauty contest

414. Major Frederick Bumble

415. Jimmy Logan

416. 1973

417. Patsy Rowlands

418. Silver

419. Augusta Prodworthy

420. Fircombe

MATCH THE CHARACTER - 2

421. Brian Oulton   Henry Bray

                                     (*Carry On Nurse*)

422. Barbara Windsor   Daphne Honeybutt

                                     (*Carry On Spying*)

423. Joan Sims   Emily Bung

                                     (*Carry On Screaming*)

424. Bernard Cribbins   Mordecai Mendoza

                                     (*Carry On Columbus*)

425.	Liz Fraser	Delia King
		(Carry On Regardless)
426.	Sid James	Sid Carter
		(Carry On Matron)
427.	Bernard Cribbins	Harold Crump
		(Carry On Spying)
428.	Angela Douglas	Doris Mann
		(Carry On Screaming)
429.	Kenneth Williams	Oliver Reckitt
		(Carry On Nurse)
430.	Patrick Mower	Sergeant Len Able
		(Carry On England)

CARRY ON DOCTOR

431.	Jasmin Broughton
432.	Frankie Howerd
433.	Borough County Hospital
434.	Jim Dale
435.	Charlie Roper
436.	Pictures of half-naked women
437.	Hattie Jacques
438.	False: 1967
439.	Barbara Windsor
440.	Kenneth Williams

LOCATIONS - 2

| 441. | Bourne End, Bucks | Carry On Emmannuelle |

442.	Park Street, Windsor, Bucks	*Carry On Loving*
443.	Southampton Docks	*Carry On Cruising*
444.	Courts Shop,	
	St. Ives High Street,	*Carry On Camping*
445.	Black Park Road	
	Fulmer, Bucks	*Carry On Cabby*
446.	Lothair Road	*Carry On Constable*
	Ealing	
447.	Car Park at Pinewood	*Carry On Abroad*
448.	11 Clarence Road, Windsor,	
	Berks	*Carry On Regardless*
449.	Farnham Common,	*Carry On Behind*
	Bucks	
450.	Odeon Cinema, Uxbridge	*Carry On At Your*
		Convenience

POT LUCK - 2

451. 23

452. False

453. 2

454. Get-u-Fit Health Farm

455. Royal Standard Music Hall

456. True

457. 177

458. Filming a scene on which he was on a moving hospital trolley

459. 2

460. 1995

CARRY ON JACK

461. Donald Houston

462. True

463. Bernard Bresslaw

464. Hook

465. Liz Fraser

466. True

467. Anton Rodgers

468. Warner-Pathé Distribution

469. True

470. Percy Herbert

CARRY ON FILMS THAT WERE NEVER MADE

471. Carry On Down Under

472. 1962

473. True

474. £500,000

475. George Layton and Jonathan Lynn

476. Carry On Nursing

477. Carry On Dallas

478. False

479. True

480. 1961

CARRY ON SPYING

481. True

482. Daphne Honeybutt

483. Kenneth Connor

484. *The Magic of Love*

485. False: he played Harold Crump; Jim Dale played Carstairs

486. *Judith Furse*

487. *34*

488. *1964*

489. Sid Colin

490. *Hancock's Half Hour*

CARRY ON PERFORMERS ON RECORD

491. True

492. *She Was*

493. Kenneth Cope and Lance Percival

494. Spring

495. Barbara Windsor

496. 'Put on a Happy Face'

497. *False*

498. *Lovely*

499. *True*

500. *Up Pompeii*

CARRY ON UP THE KHYBER

501. Julian Holloway

502. True

503. *1968*

504. Lady Ruff-Diamond

505. *16th*

506. Enlist in the Cary On army and see the world - of laughter!

507. False: she did not appear in the film

508. Sergeant Major MacNutt

509. Alexandra Dane

510. 'Larry'

MATCH THE FILM - 1

511.	Johnny Briggs plays Sporran Soldier	*Carry On Up The Khyber*
512.	Richard O'Sullivan plays Robin Stevens	*Carry On Teacher*
513.	Gerald Campion plays Andy Galloway	*Carry On Sergeant*
514.	Jill Ireland plays Jill Thompson	*Carry On Nurse*
515.	Kenneth Williams plays Francis Courtenay	*Carry On Regardless*
516.	Dorothea Phillips plays Aunt Beatrice Grubb	*Carry On Loving*
517.	Ed Devereaux plays Hook	*Carry On Jack*
518.	Bill Owen plays Corporal Bill Copping	*Carry On Sergeant*
519.	Valerie Leon plays Paula Perkins	*Carry On Girls*
520.	Betty Marsden plays Harriet Potter	*Carry On Camping*

CARRY ON CAMPING

521. 1969

522. Sid Boggle and Bernie Lugg

523. Sid James and Bernard Bresslaw

524. Paradise Camp

525. Peter Potter

526. True

527. Charles Hawtrey

528. Chayste Place

529. Tandem

530. Miss Haggard

CARRY ON UP THE JUNGLE

531. Upsidaisi

532. Frankie Howerd

533. 1970

534. Jacki Piper

535. Lubidubies

536. Kenneth Connor (as Claude Chumley)

537. 19th

538. Yemi Ajibadi

539. Lady Evelyn Bagley

540. Reuben Martin

VALERIE LEON

541. 6

542. Carry On Up The Khyber

543. True

544. 1945

545. The Spy Who Loved Me and Never Say Never Again

546. Jane Darling

547. True

548 Carry On Up The Jungle

549. £600

550.   *Carry On Matron*

CARRY ON LAUGHING WITH THE SLIMMING FACTORY

551.   **Anne Aston**

552.   **Royal Opera House, Scarborough**

553.   **Sam Cree**

554.   **Peter Butterworth**

555.   **12**

556.   **3: *Carry On Behind, Carry On Dick* and *Carry On England***

557.   **Saxon Lucas**

558.   **16 June 1976**

559.   **2**

560.   **True**

JACKI PIPER

561.   **False**

562.   ***Carry On Matron***

563.   **Birmingham**

564.   ***The Man Who Haunted Himself***

565.   **3 August**

566.   **True**

567.   **Myrtle Plummer**

568.   ***Doctor in Trouble***

569.   **She fainted**

570.   **False**

CARRY ON SCREAMING

571. Harry H. Corbett

572. 'A' certificate

573. August 1966

574. Sid James

575. *Carry On Vampire*

576. Frank Thornton

577. True

578. Joan Sims

579. 97 minutes

580. False: they were written by Myles Rudge & Ted Dick

ANGELA DOUGLAS

581. *Carry On Cowboy*

582. True

583. *Digby, the Biggest Dog in the World*

584. 4

585. Gerrards Cross, Bucks

586. True

587. *This is the Time for Love*

588. False: 29 October

589. Annie

590. *The Boys in Blue*

SALLY GEESON

591. *Bless this House*

592. Lily

593. True

594. A TV production assistant

595. Judy Geeson

596. False

597. Carol Hawkins

598. False

599. Her skirt

600. True

CHARLES HAWTREY

601. True

602. *Carry On At Your Convenience*

603. 1914

604. *Carry On Abroad*

605. William Hartnell and Bob Monkhouse (*Carry On Sergeant*)

606. James Bedsop

607. True

608. 1987

609. True

610. £3,000

PATSY ROWLANDS

611. 9

612. *Carry On Again Doctor*

613. *Carry On Loving*

614. 1934

615. *Bless this House*

616. Hortence Withering

617. *Carry On Girls*

618. False: she was credited as the Queen

619. *Carry On Abroad*

620. *Carry On Behind*

MATCH THE FILM - 2

621.	Carol Hawkins plays Marge	*Carry On Abroad*
622.	Terence Longdon plays Herbert Hall	*Carry On Constable*
623.	Kenneth Connor plays Major Leep	*Carry On Behind*
624.	Bernard Bresslaw plays Bunghit Din	*Carry On Up The Khyber*
625.	Joan Sims plays Cora Flange	*Carry On Abroad*
626.	Amanda Barrie plays Cleopatra	*Carry On Cleo*
627.	Alexei Sayle plays Aehmed	*Carry On Columbus*
628.	Kenneth Connor plays Ted Watson	*Carry On Cabby*
629.	Diana Beevers plays Penny Lee	*Carry On Teacher*
630.	Hilda Fenemore plays Rhoda Bray	*Carry On Nurse*

JOAN SIMS

631. *Carry On Nurse*

632. *Nurse Stella Dawson*

633. *True*

634. *24*

635. *1930*

636. *Esme Crowfoot*

637. *Only Fools and Horses*

132

638.   *Simon and the Witch*

639.   *On The Up*

640.   *As Time Goes By*

CARRY ON ENGLAND

641.   1976

642.   Peter Jones

643.   Kenneth Connor

644.   Pte. Alice Easy

645   28th

646   Captain Bull

647.   Larry Dann

648.   Johnny Briggs

649.   Kenneth Connor

650.   Linda Regan

CARRY ON THEMES

651.   *4*

652.   *Carry On Columbus*

653.   *4*

654.   *First World War*

655.   *True*

656.   *Historical*

657.   *False: the theme was detective adventure*

658.   *Medical*

659.   *Carry On Emmannuelle*

660.   *True*

CARRY ON FOLLOW THAT CAMEL

661. True

662. True

663. False

664. Sid James

665. Carry On Cruising

666. Anita Harris

667. Café Zig-Zig

668. Fort Zuassantneuf

669. True

670. Mustaphor Leek

BERNARD CRIBBINS

671. 3

672. Carry On Jack

673. The Wombles

674. True

675. Anything Goes

676. Perks

677. Said Fred

678. 29 December

679. Tommy the Toreador

680. Jackanory

LIZ FRASER

681. Elizabeth Winch

682. Hancock's Half Hour

683. False

684. Doris Entwhistle

685. Bunk

686. True

687. Canteen assistant

688. Sylvia Ramsden

689. 12

690. False

DILYS LAYE

691. Lila

692. Carry On Again Doctor

693. True

694. The Bed-Sit Girl

695. False

696. Pat

697. True

698. Her trousers

699. Bernard Bresslaw

700. True

CARRY ON DON'T LOSE YOUR HEAD

701. 1966

702. Joan Sims

703. True

704. 13th

705. Michael Ward

706.   Peter Butterworth

707.   The Black Fingernail (Sid James)

708.   Peter Gilmore

709.   8

710.   £5,000

ACTORS - 1

711.   Ronnie Stevens

712.   George Roderick

713.   Frankie Howerd

714.   Arnold Ridley

715.   Jon Pertwee

716.   Nicholas Parsons

717.   Nosher Powell

718.   Sid James

719.   Albert Moses

720.   Francis de Wolff

BERNARD BRESSLAW

721.   *Carry On Cowboy*

722.   *The Army Game*

723.   *Carry On Behind*

724.   1934

725.   Bernie Hulke

726.   14

727.   *Carry On Follow That Camel*

728.   Sir Roger Daley

729.   £2,500

730.   Ken Biddle

CARRY ON LOVING

731.   An undertaker's assistant

732.   Kenneth Williams

733.   Imogen Hassall

734.   The Wedded Bliss Agency

735.   Milk bottle tops

736.   Sid James and Kenneth Williams

737.   Jacki Piper

738.   1970

739.   Patricia Franklin

740.   Carry On Henry

LESLIE PHILLIPS

741.   4

742.   False

743   Lara Croft: Tomb Raider

744.   Alistair Grigg

745.   Venus

746.   1924

747.   £720

748.   Carry On Columbus

749.   OBE

750.   Love on a Branch Line

ROBIN ASKWITH

751. *Carry On Girls*

752. *True*

753. *All 4*

754. *True*

755. *Dead Funny*

756. *The Confessions of Robin Askwith*

757. *The Bottle Boys*

758. *False*

759. *On The House*

760. *True*

CARRY ON CATCHPHRASES

761. *"Oh! Hello!"*

762. *"Stop messin' about!"*

763. *"I only arsked"*

764. *"Cor blimey!"*

765. *"Ding dong!"*

766. *"Frying tonight!"*

767. *"Oh matron!"*

768. *False*

769. *"Pound!"*

770. *"Infamy! Infamy! They've all got it in for me!"*

CARRY ON SCRIPTWRITERS

771. *20*

772. *False*

773. *Carry On Behind* and *Carry On Columbus*

774. Eric Merriman

775. True

776. John Antrobus

777. Lew Schwarz

778. True

779. Ian Grant

780. False

CARRY ON CHARACTER NAMES

781. True

782. Albert Potter

783. *Carry On Again Doctor*

784. Ha Ha

785. Maureen

786. Alexandra Dane

787. Mrs Spragg

788. Linda Upmore

789. *Carry On Cowboy*

790. Ameila Baynton

RICHARD O'SULLIVAN

791. Beryl Reid

792. *Robin's Nest*

793. *Me & My Girl*

794. False

795. 7 May

796.   *French Fields*

797.   *True*

798.   *The Young Ones*

799.   *Futtock's End*

800.   *12*

CARRY ON MATRON

801.   **Jack Douglas**

802.   **Kenneth Williams**

803.   **1972**

804.   **Kenneth Cope**

805.   **True**

806.   **Hattie Jacques**

807.   **True**

808.   *Carry On Abroad*

809.   **Finisham Maternity Hospital**

810.   **Frances Kemp**

ACTRESSES - 1

811.   **Marianne Stone**

812.   **Edina Ronay**

813.   *Carry On Camping* and *Carry On Behind*

814.   **Anna Karen**

815.   **Patricia Hayes**

816.   **Judith Furse**

817.   **Heather Emmanuel**

818.   **Adrienne Posta**

819. *Wanda Ventham*

820. *Ambrosine Phillpotts*

CARRY ON COWBOY

821. *Sid James*

822. *True*

823. *1965*

824. *Sid James and Kenneth Williams*

825. *Carry On Screaming*

826. *Angela Douglas*

827. *True*

828. *Stodge City*

829. *Jim Dale*

830. *True*

KENNETH WILLIAMS

831. *Carry On Sergeant*

832. *James Bailey*

833. *25*

834. *Emile Prevert*

835. *Carry On Spying*

836. *Cabaret*

837. *"Oh, stop messin' about!"*

838. *£5,000*

839. *Carry On Follow That Camel*

840. *62*

FRANKIE HOWERD

841. 2

842. *Carry On Doctor* and *Carry On Up The Jungle*

843. Francis Bigger

844. OBE

845. *The Great St Trinian's Train Robbery*

846. *The Mouse on the Moon*

847. True

848. *The Runaway Bus*

849. *1917*

850. *Carry On Columbus*

SHIRLEY EATON

851. *Carry On Constable*

852. Max Bygraves

853. *Goldfinger*

854. *1968*

855. True

856. *Carry On Regardless*

857. False

858. Eric

859. Canteen girl

860. True

CARRY ON AT PINEWOOD STUDIOS

861. 8

862. Sir Donald Sinden

863. *True*

864. *Behind the carpenter's workshops*

865. *Carry On Nurse*

866. *True*

867. *The corridor that leads to the Archive Department*

868. *A and C*

869. *Audrey Skinner*

870. *False*

CARRY ON BEHIND THE CAMERA

871. *True*

872. *Stella Rivers*

873. *Leah Bracknell*

874. *False*

875. *Alan Hume*

876. *Gina Jay*

877. *15*

878. *True*

879. *Bert Batt*

880. *Malcolm McLaren and Lee Gorman*

CARRY ON CAST BIRTHDAYS

881. *1916*

882. *Hounslow*

883. *15 August*

884. *26 April 1927*

885. *True*

886.   9 May 1930

887.   1927

888.   1917

889.   1919

890.   Patsy Rowlands

JUNE WHITFIELD

891.   Carry On Behind

892.   Bless This House

893.   Eth

894.   True

895.   Suzy Aitchison

896.   True

897.   The News Huddlines

898.   11 November

899.   The Blood Donor

900.   True

ACTRESSES - 2

901.   Molly Weir

902.   Olga Lowe

903.   Christine Rodgers

904.   Jean St Clair

905.   Louise Burton

906.   Tricia Newby

907.   Elspeth March

908.   Joan Sims

909. Sheila Hancock

910. Monica Dietrich

CARRY ON CLEO

911. Amanda Barrie

912. 1964

913. The funniest film since 54 B.C.

914. Kenneth Williams

915. Sid James and Kenneth Williams

916. Joan Sims

917. 9th

918. *Carry On Spying*

919. Victor Maddern

920. Julius Caesar (Kenneth Williams)

MATCH THE DATE - 4

921.	Joy Harrington was born	1914
922.	The first *Carry On Christmas* was shown	1969
923.	Richard O'Brien was born	1942
924.	The *Carry On Laughing* series started	1975
925.	The first *Carry On* film was released	1958
926.	Wendy Richard was born	1946
927.	Henry Livings sadly passed away	1998
928.	*Carry On Camping* was released	1969
929.	Joe Robinson was born	1929
930.	Jack Shampan sadly passed away	1989

CARRY ON AT YOUR CONVENIENCE

931.   1971

932.   Kenneth Williams

933.   Peter Burton

934.   Vic Spanner

935.   Richard O'Callaghan

936.   Joey

937.   Brighton

938.   1870

939.   Joan Sims

940.   Carry On Henry

ACTORS - 2

941.   Patrick Cargill

942.   Peter Butterworth

943.   Victor Maddern

944.   Ian Curry

945.   Brian Coburn

946.   Larry Dann

947.   Kenneth Williams

948.   Ted Ray

949.   Bill Owen

950.   Peter Jones

POT LUCK - 3

951.   True

952.   Carry On Jungle Boy

953.   Danny Robin

954.   Paula Perkins

955.   Michael Caine

956.   Brian Wilde

957.   Kenny Lynch

958.   Peggy Ann Clifford

959.   Olga Lowe

960.   A gong

CARRY ON BOOKS

961.   1988

962.   False: it was written by Barbara Windsor and Adrian Rigelsford

963.   *High Spirits*

964.   Roger Lewis

965.   Russell Davies

966.   *The Complete Sid James*

967.   False: it is called *And June Whitfield*

968.   Jack Douglas

969.   Morris Bright and Robert Ross

970.   1985

BOB MONKHOUSE

971.   False

972.   *Dentist On the Job*

973.   Shirley Eaton

974.   Charlie Sage

975.   False

976. *Bob Says Opportunity Knocks*

977. *Every Second Counts*

978. *Bob's Full House*

979. *Crying With Laughter*

980. *True*

POT LUCK - 4

981. *Joan Hickson*

982. *The Mike Sammes Singers*

983. *True*

984. *Philip Stone*

985. *True*

986. *Shirley Stelfox*

987. *Robin*

988. *True*

989. *Bread*

990. *Bill Kenwright*

ERIC ROGERS

991. *13*

992. *Oliver!*

992. *Sunday Night at the London Palladium*

993. *22*

995. *False*

996. *Genevieve*

997. *True*

998. *Steptoe and Son*

999. *Piano*

1000. *False*

OTHER BOOKS BY CHRIS COWLIN:

* Celebrities' Favourite Football Teams

* The British TV Sitcom Quiz Book

* The Cricket Quiz Book

* The Gooners Quiz Book

* The Horror Film Quiz Book

* The Official Aston Villa Quiz Book

* The Official Birmingham City Quiz Book

* The Official Brentford Quiz Book

* The Official Bristol Rovers Quiz Book

* The Official Burnley Quiz Book

* The Official Bury Quiz Book

* The Official Carlisle United Quiz Book

* The Official Carry On Quiz Book

* The Official Chesterfield Football Club Quiz Book

* The Official Colchester United Quiz Book

* The Official Coventry City Quiz Book

* The Official Doncaster Rovers Quiz Book

* The Official Greenock Morton Quiz Book

* The Official Heart of Midlothian Quiz Book

* The Official Hereford United Quiz Book

* The Official Hull City Quiz Book

* The Official Ipswich Town Quiz Book

OTHER BOOKS BY CHRIS COWLIN:

* The Official Leicester City Quiz Book

* The Official Macclesfield Town Quiz Book

* The Official Norwich City Football Club Quiz

* The Official Notts County Quiz Book

* The Official Peterborough United Quiz Book

* The Official Port Vale Quiz Book

* The Official Queen of the South Quiz Book

* The Official Rochdale AFC Quiz Book

* The Official Rotherham United Quiz Book

* The Official Sheffield United Quiz Book

* The Official Shrewsbury Town Quiz Book

* The Official Stockport County Quiz Book

* The Official Walsall Football Club Quiz Book

* The Official Watford Football Club Quiz Book

* The Official West Bromwich Albion Quiz Book

* The Official Wolves Quiz Book

* The Official Yeovil Town Quiz Book

* The Reality Television Quiz Book

* The Southend United Quiz Book

* The Spurs Quiz Book

* The Sunderland AFC Quiz Book

* The Ultimate Derby County Quiz Book

* The West Ham United Quiz Book

www.apexpublishing.co.uk